Anna's Six Wishes

MARGRIT CRUICKSHANK

Anna's Six Wishes

MARGRIT CRUICKSHANK

POOLBEG

Published in 1995 by
Poolbeg Press Ltd
Knocksedan House,
123 Baldoyle Industrial Estate,
Dublin 13, Ireland
Reprinted 1997

A catalogue record for this book is available from the British Library.

ISBN 1 85371 510 7

Illustrations by Marie Louise Fitzpatrick
Cover design by Poolbeg Group Services Ltd
Set by Poolbeg Group Services in Times 12/18
Printed by The Guernsey Press Ltd,
Vale, Guernsey, Channel Islands.

About the Author

Award-winning author, Margrit Cruickshank, is perhaps best known for her popular *S.K.U.N.K.* series. *S.K.U.N.K. and the Ozone Conspiracy* was short-listed for the Irish Book Award (Young People's Book Medal) in 1990. She was short-listed for the Bisto Book Award in 1991, and again in 1992, and was the winner of the 1993 Reading Association of Ireland Special Merit Book of the Year Award for her young adult novel, *Circling the Triangle*.

By the same author

Circling the Triangle
A Monster called Charlie

S.K.U.N.K. and the Ozone Conspiracy
S.K.U.N.K. and the Splitting Earth
S.K.U.N.K. and the Nuclear Waste Plot
S.K.U.N.K. and the Freak Flood Fiasco

To Shane, Aisling and Bebhinn

Contents

Anna's First Wish:
The Ice Cream Cone

Anna Byrne was doing her homework when a big, black, hairy spider came out from behind her spelling book and walked across the table towards her.

Anna was eight. She lived with her parents, her brother Mark who was fourteen, and her cat Tiptoes who was exactly one year, seven months and three days. Nothing very special ever seemed to happen to Anna, Mark, or even Tiptoes. Nothing very special – until this particular afternoon.

It was hot. Very, very hot. The kind of day when you dream of jumping into a cool, clear swimming pool and long for an ice cream. Anna had read the words in her spelling book from the top to the bottom, from the bottom to the top, and from the top to the bottom again. She had never been so bored.

And then this spider walked out from behind her book.

"Yuck!" Anna said.

She pushed back her chair and grabbed her English copy.

The spider glared at her. "And just what do you think you're doing?" it asked in a squeaky, angry, spidery sort of voice.

Anna guiltily hid the copy behind her back.

"You were just about to squash me into a squidgy black blob," it accused her.

One part of Anna's mind told her that there's nothing wrong with squashing spiders into squidgy black blobs. Another part told her that spiders don't speak. But, instead of saying any of this, she found herself stuttering, "Oh no, I wasn't!"

"Oh yes, you were!" said the spider. "Just because I'm black and hairy and I crawl. Isn't that right?"

Anna blushed.

"Well, let me tell you, you great, big, lumpy, horrible, white, *human* thing, other spiders find me beautiful. So there!"

Anna let her copy drop on to the chair behind her.

"Well?" the spider asked.

"Well, what?"

"You could at least say you're sorry."

Anna wasn't. Not really. But she muttered "Sorry" all the same.

"That's better," said the spider. "Now that you're beginning to show some manners, I can tell you why I'm here. I'm your fairy-godmother."

"You're *what*?" The only fairy-godmother

Anna knew was Cinderella's. And Cinderella's fairy-godmother was a pretty lady in a fluffy pink dress who wore a diamond tiara on her head and had wings growing out of her shoulders. Not a great black hairy spider who thought that she was beautiful.

"I'm your fairy-godmother," repeated the spider. "And I'm here to tell you that you can have three wishes."

Anna stared at it. "You have to be kidding," she said.

The spider shrugged its eight shoulders. "Whatever you say."

If this was a dream, Anna thought, it was a very real one. "Why only three wishes?" she asked. "If you're that clever, why not make it ten? Or a hundred? Or a million billion trillion *squillion* wishes?"

"Oh, all right, then," said the spider. "I'll give you six. But that's my final offer. And don't go thinking you can make any of them my-wish-is-to-be-granted-any-wish-I-like-from-now-until-forever. That's been tried and it doesn't work."

Anna still didn't believe this was happening to her. What *would* she wish for, if she really had a fairy-godmother? "I'd like," she said slowly, " a tape-recorder . . . and new shoes . . . and lunch at MacDonald's . . ." she found she was getting the hang of it, "and a trip to the Zoo and a television of my own and a new bike and a puppy and a pony and a model aeroplane that flies," she went on, "and for Granny to come and give me five pounds and for all my homework to be done for me by magic and for a digital watch and . . ."

"That's more than six," interrupted the spider. "Also, I forgot to tell you: you can't have them all at once. You only get one at a time. So start again. And this time, think of what you *really* want. Six wishes for the rest of your life: it's not something to be wasted on junk, you know."

Anna began to wonder if the spider could actually, after all, be serious. Maybe you *could* have a spider as a fairy-godmother? Maybe you could have six wishes? And yet . . .

"I think you're trying to make me look stupid," she said.

"Would I waste my time?" asked the spider. "Either you make a wish or you don't; it's no skin off my nose."

Anna wondered if spiders had noses. She didn't think it was a good time to ask, though.

"But if you're going to wish for something," the spider went on, "this is what you have to do. Decide what you *really* want and then say:

"Please, fairy-godmother, beautiful as can be, will you grant this wish for me?

"Then *I* say:

"Indeed I will, so tell it fast.

And may this wish not be your last.

"Then *you* say: *I wish* . . . and shut your eyes.

"Have you got that?"

It sounded very complicated. "Please, fairy-godmother . . ." Anna started to giggle. Once she had started, she just couldn't stop.

"Pull yourself together!" snapped the spider. *"Please, fairy-godmother, beautiful as can be . . ."* it prompted.

"Do I really have to say that?" asked Anna.

"Yes. Now, have you decided what to wish for?"

Anna hadn't. Shc tried to think of what she wanted most of all. But there were so many things she wanted. And it was so hot. If only . . .

That was it!

"I'd like . . ." she started.

"You have a mind like a hen!" snapped the spider. "What did I tell you to say?"

Anna took a deep breath. She felt a complete idiot. "Please, fairy-godmother," she recited, trying to keep a straight face, "beautiful as can be, will you grant this wish for me?"

The spider heaved a great sigh, looked up at the ceiling and answered, in a *very* bored voice: "Indeed I will, so tell it fast. And may this wish not be your last."

"I wish . . ." Anna hesitated. The spider had warned her not to waste her wishes on junk, but she couldn't resist it. Just for one wish. After all, she'd still have five left.

"I wish for the biggest ice cream cone in the whole world!"

She shut her eyes and held out her hand.

Nothing happened.

She told herself she wasn't surprised. After

all, she hadn't really believed all that fairy-godmother stuff anyway.

Opening her eyes, she found that it had suddenly gone dark.

She groped for the light switch beside the door and turned it on. The spider had vanished. And there wasn't an ice cream cone anywhere.

So much for that, she thought. I suppose I'd better get on with my homework.

Then she looked at the window. Instead of a view of the front garden, all she could see was a sheet of what looked like brown cardboard, shutting out the light.

She poked it with a finger. Her finger went right through the cardboard stuff into something cold and wet. She took her finger out and licked it. It was ice cream!

Not daring to believe what had happened, she raced downstairs and out into the garden. There, planted right in the middle of the front lawn, was the biggest, most enormous, huge, towering, mountainous, immense, gigantic ice cream cone ever!

She craned her neck and looked up at the

top of it. Even if she were an expert mountain climber – which she wasn't – there was no way she'd be able to get up there to lick it. Not even the fire brigade had a ladder that high.

She raced back up to her bedroom. "Spider! Fairy-godmother! Whatever you are!" she shouted. "Come back! I've made a mistake! I want to change my wish!"

But no spider appeared.

She noticed a trickle of ice cream oozing out of the hole she'd poked with her finger. It gathered into a puddle on the window ledge and then started to drip, with little sticky plops, on to the carpet beneath. She licked the ice cream coming out of the hole. It tasted great! She licked some more. She found she had to lick faster as the ice cream flowed more quickly. It was all over her mouth now and was getting up her nose and into her hair – and still a good bit of it was dripping on to the sill and falling into the room.

She'd have to get help.

She grabbed an old jumper and dumped it on the carpet to catch the drips, had a last look round for the spider and ran to fetch her brother Mark who was supposed to be minding her. He was sitting in front of the TV watching a cartoon. She dragged him out into the garden.

To her horror, a crowd had already gathered. People were standing on the flower-beds, some were leaning on the gate, others were trampling the lawn . . . And they were all gawping up at the gigantic ice cream cone.

"Wow!" said Mark. "Where did that come from?"

"I don't know," said Anna, more or less truthfully. "Help me to get rid of it before Mum and Dad come home."

Mark prodded it with a finger, as Anna had done earlier. Ice cream started to drip through the hole he'd made.

Mrs O'Flaherty from next door pushed forward and tried a bit. "It's real!" she shouted, licking her fingers. "Claire! Go and get a bucket!"

In an instant, the crowd had disappeared.

"Think of somehing!" Anna pleaded. "Quick! Before they all come back!"

Mark gave the cone a shove. It didn't move. "We could try to get hold of a bulldozer," he suggested. "Or some dynamite."

Anna giggled. Then she heard a noise behind them. She turned round.

The crowd had come back. Hundreds of people were pounding down the road towards them and they were all carrying some sort of container. Some had plastic buckets, some had metal pails, some had square plastic boxes, some had bowls, some had pots and pans, and someone had even brought the baby's bath. They all pushed and shoved their way through the Byrnes' front gate and headed for the ice cream cone.

Mr Kelly had brought a knife. He cut a neat round hole near the base of the cone and started to scoop the ice cream out into a red plastic bucket.

"Here, can I borrow that?" Mrs Quinn grabbed the knife and cut another hole further round the cone.

Mrs O'Flaherty from next door snatched the knife from her and slashed a huge tear in the cone. "Come on, Claire. Get to work!" Anna noticed that she had brought two buckets and that each was full of empty plastic boxes. Trust Mrs O'Flaherty, she thought.

Soon the whole base of the cone had been hacked away and people were filling their containers from the flood of ice cream oozing out.

"Hey! They're getting all of it!" Mark shouted. "Come on!"

Anna followed him into the kitchen where they grabbed as many pots and bowls as they could carry. As the people in the garden scooped the ice cream from the bottom of the cone, Anna and Mark stood at the bedroom window and collected as much as they could from the top, running up and down to the freezer whenever their containers were full.

Once the freezer was packed to the top, they stopped.

They looked over the window ledge and watched the people scrabbling about underneath. Soon, only a melting lump of muddy, trampled ice cream was left. Anna gave the cone a push. It swayed away from the window and back towards the house. She gave it another push. The third time she pushed it, it crumpled like a collapsing chimney-stack on to the heads of the people beneath.

Mrs O'Flaherty tried a piece. "That's real wafer, that is!" she shouted.

In an instant, everyone was piling it on to the tops of their containers, cramming it inside their jackets and stuffing it into their pockets. Then they picked up their buckets and bowls and headed for home.

Anna looked down. The garden was a *mess*! "How do we explain that?" she asked.

"I don't know," said Mark helpfully. "And here comes Mum now."

Mrs Byrne stopped at the garden gate and looked at the puddles of ice cream and bits of wafer sinking slowly into the muddy patch that had once been her lawn. Then she saw Anna and Mark at the window.

"Come down here," she ordered. "Just what has been going on?"

Anna tried to think of some reasonable explanation on the way downstairs, but couldn't. She decided to tell the truth. "You see, Mum, I've got this fairy-godmother who's a spider and it said I could ask for anything I wanted and I asked for an ice cream and . . ."

Mrs Byrne withered her with a look. "That's enough, Anna. Mark, tell me what happened."

Mark opened his eyes wide and put on his most innocent expression. "Well, it was like this, Mum. There was suddenly this great heap of ice cream in the garden. I honestly don't know how it got there. Maybe a spaceship from Mars dropped it . . ." He caught his mother's eye. "Or maybe it fell off an ice cream lorry. Anyway, everyone for miles around came to get some and they all trampled the garden. Honest, Mum, it wasn't our fault. We couldn't stop them. And we did try to save as much of it as we could for you."

Mrs Byrne never did find out exactly what had happened. Neither did the neighbours, nor the police when they were brought in, not even the RTE television crew nor the reporters from the *Evening Press*. Anna was the only one who knew – and she had more sense than to tell anyone.

She just couldn't wait, though, to see the spider again and get her next wish!

Anna's Second Wish: The Dragon Greenspikes

Days went by. Weeks. Still Anna waited for her fairy-godmother to appear and grant another wish. And still, no matter how nice she was to spiders (big round hairy ones, huge black skinny ones, little tiny scampering ones, spiders in webs, spiders on the ceiling, spiders in the bath), not one of them spoke a single, solitary word to her.

A fairy-godmother wouldn't promise another five wishes and then just disappear, would she? Anna asked herself.

She thought of all the things that could have happened to the spider. It could have been sucked up in the vacuum cleaner. Or squidged under somebody's shoes, or flushed down the toilet.

Spiders, she realised, led very dangerous lives.

And then, one Saturday morning, when she was alone in the kitchen making a triple-decker nut-and-chocolate-spread sandwich, she heard a noise behind her. She looked round.

A tiny little mouse with short brown fur and a long tapering tail was sitting on the worktop, nibbling a chocolate-covered hazelnut.

"Shoo!" she said. She shook her knife at it. A blob of nut-and-chocolate spread left the blade, sailed over the sink and splattered against the window. "Go away, you dirty, horrible thing!"

The mouse calmly swallowed the last bit of nut, wiped its whiskers *and spoke*.

"You'll never learn," it said.

Anna jumped. It sounded just like her fairy-godmother.

"Anyway, who are you calling dirty?" the mouse asked. "*I* haven't just thrown food at the window."

"I . . . I . . . I didn't know it was you," Anna mumbled.

"Obviously," sniffed the mouse. "Have you thought of another wish yet?"

Anna had dreamed up a hundred different wishes in the past few weeks, but now her mind went blank. She couldn't think of anything. Certainly not anything that would be worth using a magic wish for.

"Get a move on," snapped the mouse. "I haven't got all day. If you can't think of a wish by the time I've cleaned my whiskers, the whole contract's off."

Anna panicked. "Please, fairy-godmother . . ." What was it she had to say? "Please, fairy-godmother, beautiful as can be, will you grant this wish for me?"

"I suppose I'll have to. So tell it fast and may this wish not be your last."

"I wish . . ." Anna thought desperately. Then she remembered a really exciting book she'd been reading, about fearless knights rescuing fair maidens from fierce, fire-breathing dragons. Why couldn't she do it the other way around? "I wish to have an adventure and kill a dragon and rescue a handsome prince!" she said.

The mouse looked disappointed. "That's it then? That's the best you can do?" It sighed. "Okay, so shut your eyes and away you go. Only remember, it was your idea. Don't blame me if you don't like it."

Anna shut her eyes.

When she opened them again, she was on a hillside overlooking a beautiful wild valley. A sparkling (what else?) river wound between lush flower-studded meadows towards the distant blue line of the sea. Away to her left, the turrets of a castle poked out above a forest of trees. Beneath her, on the riverbank, a small town huddled round a ford.

There was something on her head, though, that made it difficult to see. She tried to raise a hand to find out what it was, but her arm was all stiff and heavy. And it clanked. She moved a leg. It clanked too. She looked down. She was wearing armour!

Her feet were encased in narrow pointy metal shoes, her hands in awkward metal gloves, her legs and arms in metal pipes and her body in a sort of body stocking of scratchy chain mail with what felt like half a coal scuttle buckled across her front and the other half across her back. On her head was a heavy metal helmet with a sort of pointy beak for her nose and two slits for her eyes. And, in one of her gloved hands, she held a long sword.

Something suddenly butted her in the back. She almost jumped out of the suit of armour.

"Hurry up, my lady," said a deep voice behind her. "The fair Lord Henry awaits thy help. Wouldst thou leave him to the mercy of the dragon Greenspikes?"

Anna turned round – with a great deal of difficulty. She found herself looking up at an enormous brown cart-horse. It was at least twice, more probably *three* times, as high as she was. Although it had spoken softly, she didn't at all like the look of its huge hair-fringed hooves. Or the way its lips curled back from its massive front teeth.

Why couldn't the mouse have given her a Shetland pony?

"Approach thee to yon stile, my lady, and mount me there," suggested the horse, moving to a wooden stile at the edge of the forest. "There is no time to be lost."

Anna clanked her way across to the stile and clambered up it. She felt like a small one-woman tank. By the time she had reached the top step, she was exhausted.

The horse waited quietly as she grabbed the reins around its neck and, holding as tightly as she could to its coarse dusty mane, raised one heavy leg and managed, just, to get it over the top of the saddle.

"Dally not, my lady," encouraged the horse. "Thou art almost there. One good heave and thou wilt be mounted. But prithee take care," it added quickly, "not to heave too much or thou wilt fall in a heap on the other side."

Anna saw what it meant. The ground was a very long way away. She gritted her teeth, held even more tightly on to the horse's mane and pulled herself up into the saddle. For a minute she swayed dangerously from one side to the other, but then she got her balance, found the stirrups, slid her pointy metal shoes into them, took the reins between her metal-covered fingers and sat up.

"*Very* good, my lady," said the horse. "Now let us make haste to rescue the fair Lord Henry."

"Er . . . could we not make too much haste, just for the moment?" Anna asked. "I'm not used to riding."

"Don't say anything," muttered the horse to itself. "Just don't say anything. Why do I always get the beginners?" It started to plod towards the distant castle.

Anna relaxed. Riding was quite easy, really; a bit like sitting on a rather bumpy armchair. It was fun to bounce along, high above the ground and look through the slits in her helmet at the scenery.

Then the sun began to heat up her armour. She grew hotter and hotter. She felt herself sweating. How had knights survived without air-conditioning in their coats of mail? she wondered, trying to wipe her brow and thumping her helmet with a metal arm instead. If she didn't get somewhere cool soon, she'd be roasted to a frazzle without ever meeting a dragon.

A dragon . . . !

"About this Lord Henry," she said. "Do we really have to go and rescue him?" Somehow, now that she was actually *in* the adventure, the idea of having to fight a fire-breathing dragon didn't seem quite as attractive as it had done in the safety of her kitchen at home.

"Why yes, forsooth. Wouldst thou be known as a cowardly maid, not brave enough to save a knight in distress?"

"Maybe," said Anna. "It depends."

"Thou art in verity kidding me, I hope," muttered the horse, "so let us get on with it. Hold on, Lady Anna!"

The horse seemed to put itself into a higher gear. Anna threw her arms round its neck and clung on, wishing she had a few more hands. Spiders were lucky, she couldn't help thinking. And octopuses. She felt as if she were perched on top of a barrel in a stormy sea. Miles beneath her, the ground bounced by under the horse's galumphing hooves.

Then, as suddenly as they'd started, they stopped.

In front of them was a rocky cliff. At the base of the cliff yawned the black entrance to a cave. In front of the cave was . . . Anna blinked. It was her brother, Mark, tied to a stake! And in front of Mark was a ferocious, fire-breathing, smoke-belching dragon!

Anna shut her eyes. When she opened them again, Mark and the dragon were still there. She looked round, without much hope, for the mouse. What she needed now was another wish.

And then she remembered. She had said she wanted to *kill* a dragon and *rescue* a handsome knight. So, if her wish was to be granted, she must be meant, somehow or other, to kill the dragon and stay alive to have her other four wishes.

"It's all right, Mark," she said, hoping that she sounded more confident than she felt. "I've come to rescue you."

"I am not Mark," said the knight who looked like Mark. "I am Lord Henry, son of King Pelidor who lives in yon castle yonder. I should be much obliged if you *would* rescue me – it gets a bit boring, being tied up like this."

The dragon turned slowly and looked at Anna. It shut its mouth, so that the fire disappeared. When it opened it again, only a trickle of smoke seeped out from between its huge pointy teeth.

"I assume you've come to kill me," it said mournfully.

"Go on, my lady," hissed the horse. "Tell it what's what, forsooth."

Anna hesitantly raised her sword. (You think this is easy? You try it! Her metal gloves didn't grip all that well and the pipes round her arms made it difficult to bend them. On top of which, the sword weighed a ton.)

The dragon watched her sadly. Tears trickled out of its fierce red eyes and hissed into steam as they ran down its hot scaly cheeks. It laid its head on the ground.

"That's the way, my lady," the horse urged excitedly. "Go on! Smite the foul fiend dead!"

Anna looked down at the dragon. The dragon looked up at Anna. "We'd better get it over with," it sighed. "Can you reach or shall I move a bit nearer?"

"I can't just kill you," Anna said. "Shouldn't we have a fight or something first?" It wasn't that she *wanted* to fight the dragon, only it seemed fairer somehow. Even though she knew she had to win in the end.

"Oh, get on with it," complained Prince Henry. "Don't just stand around yakking, the two of you."

"I'm tired of fighting," said the dragon. "I'm tired of having to threaten people and get them to tie up their sons and daughters for me to eat. I don't even *like* eating people. I'd much prefer lettuce or celery or strawberries – even a nice bit of cabbage. But they don't listen."

"Do you mean we've been sacrificing people for months for *nothing*?" asked the prince.

The dragon pouted. "It's been a sacrifice for me too, you know."

"Then why did you do it?"

"Your city councillors seemed to expect it of me and I like to try to be helpful. But I haven't enjoyed it. Not one little bit."

The horse raised its head and gave a disgusted whinny. Anna had to grab its mane to stay on.

"Come on, horse," she coaxed. "Just take me to that rock over there so that I can get down."

"You're going to fight the dragon after all, then?" The horse cheered up again.

"No," said Anna firmly.

And then a thought struck her. She'd made

a wish to *kill* a dragon. If she didn't kill one, *would she ever get home*?

She'd have to worry about that later, she told herself as she slid, clanking, off the horse, tumbled painfully from the rock to the ground and lumbered, still clanking, over to cut the prince's ropes with her sword.

Prince Henry didn't even bother to thank her. He rubbed his wrists, turned to the dragon and helped it up.

"It's all right," he said encouragingly. "I'll tell my father, the king, how you feel and you can live in the palace with us and I'll feed you lettuce and celery and strawberries."

"And cabbage?" asked the dragon.

"And cabbage," agreed the prince. "You can be my pet. Not many princes have pet dragons. And I can make people pay to come and see you. That'll be nice."

"It will?" asked the dragon doubtfully.

"Think of the lettuce and celery and strawberries," said Anna. "Not to mention the cabbage."

The dragon stopped crying. Its monstrous

face split into a gentle smile. "And I won't have to live in a wet old cave any more and eat people? Oh, goody! Can we go now?"

The horse looked from Anna to Prince Henry and back to Anna again. It semed to be trying to make up its mind. Then it lumbered over to stand beside the prince.

"Accept, oh noble lord, my homage as thine own true steed," it said, bowing its head. "Okay, if there were anyone else about, I doubt if I'd have chosen thee for a master. But beggars cannot be choosers. And I will never, *never*, NEVER," it threw Anna a filthy look, "be a warhorse to a craven coward! Hop on, oh fair prince," it added, "and I shall bear thee whither thou desirest."

Before Anna could stop them, the prince, who still looked so like Mark it was unbelievable, was galloping off on the horse while the dragon, its tail in the air, its nostrils sending out puffs of smoke like a Red Indian's smoke signal, trotted happily after them.

"Hey, wait a minute!" Anna shouted. "What about me?"

They didn't even look back.

She clanked down sadly on the grass. Now what? she thought.

"I suppose you didn't do too badly," said a familiar voice.

Anna looked round. The mouse was sitting on the rock beside her, cleaning its whiskers again. "I wasn't too thrilled with that *I want to kill a dragon* bit; there's far too much violence in the world today. But you did rescue the knight. Shall we call it another wish gone?"

"Oh yes," said Anna. "Please."

"Fine, then. See you around."

Just like that, the river, the valley, the forest and the cave were gone and Anna found herself in her own kitchen again.

The back door opened and Mark came in, swinging his schoolbag.

"Thank goodness you got home safely too," she said.

"Why? What's up?"

Anna didn't answer. At least everything had turned out all right in the end, she thought.

She really would have to be more careful with her next wish, she decided, flicking a long brown horsehair from her sleeve into the bin.

Anna's Third Wish: The Great Detective

"There's been a mouse in here!" exclaimed Mrs Byrne the next morning as she took the breakfast cereal out of the cupboard. "Do you see these droppings? And look what it's done to the cereal box! I'll have to set a trap."

"No!" Anna yelped in alarm. "I mean, you can't! I mean, mice are creatures like anything else. They have to eat too, don't they?"

"Not my breakfast cereal, they don't," said Mrs Byrne. "*And* they spread germs. I'll buy a mouse-trap when I'm in town today."

Anna was very relieved when the trap caught nothing. Her fairy-godmother had disappeared again.

She thought about what to wish for next. She also smiled at every spider she came across and waited expectantly if she saw *any* small animal, just in case.

This made life a bit complicated. Every time she noticed an insect, or a bird, or even a cat or a dog in the street, she'd stop and stare at it, trying to look as if she loved it, hoping it would speak to her and grant her another wish.

"I'm worried about Anna," Mrs Byrne told Mr Byrne. "She seems to be spaced out all the time. She can't walk from one end of the garden to the other without going into a daydream every couple of steps."

"It's the age she's at," Mr Byrne muttered as he slapped paste on to another piece of wallpaper. "I feel for her. At the age *I'm* at, I hate hanging wallpaper. We should have paid someone else to do this."

"You're not hanging it, I am," said Mrs Byrne from the top of the ladder. "And, at the salary we're both at, we'll have to do it ourselves for a good while longer."

Mark was more direct. "You've finally

flipped," he told his sister. "You look like some mad alien, going around chatting up every animal you meet with that stupid grin on your face all the time."

Anna didn't care. The next time her fairy-godmother appeared, she was determined to be ready.

One evening, Mr and Mrs Byrne were out, Mark was at Scouts and Claire had come round from next door to baby-sit. Anna liked Claire. Claire let her stay up late and watch anything she wanted on TV.

That evening, there was a funny film on, about a detective who kept getting things mixed up and bumping into furniture, or falling into fountains and out of windows. They were both laughing so much that neither of them thought of the time until the film was over.

"Look at the clock!" Claire shrieked. "Your parents'll be home any minute. They'll kill me! Get up to bed!"

Anna didn't mind being sent upstairs. She was really very tired. She pulled off her clothes, dumped them in a heap on the floor, pulled on her pyjamas, decided that her face and teeth could wait till morning and crawled into bed.

She was just falling asleep when she heard a buzzing noise. It seemed to be in the room with her. She pulled the duvet over her ears and turned on to her other side. The buzzing got worse. She shut her eyes tightly and tried to ignore it. The buzzing wouldn't go away. She sat up.

A bluebottle was flying in circles just above her pillow!

Anna jumped out of bed, grabbed a book from her bedside table, raised it . . .

"Bussssbees!" buzzed the bluebottle, dodging out of her reach. "There you go again, trying to bludgeon me! I had hoped you'd have learnt your lesson. Silly of me, really."

"Fairy-godmother!" Anna sank back down on her bed and let the book fall into her lap. "I thought you weren't coming back. It's been ages."

The bluebottle settled itself on her duvet. "Has it? I hadn't noticed."

"Two weeks and four days."

"Typical," buzzed the bluebottle bitterly. "You keep me bustling about long past my bedtime, waiting for you to come up to bed. Then you try to behead me. And then you bleat on about *my* behaviour. I sometimes wonder why I bother."

"I didn't mean to complain," Anna said quickly. "And I'm sorry if I tried to . . . er . . . I didn't think. I was almost asleep . . ."

"Bosh!" said the bluebottle.

Anna blushed.

"Well?" the bluebottle demanded briskly. "Are you going to bring yourself to beg for a wish or not? You should remember what to do by now. Or do I have to tell you again?" It heaved its six shoulders. "I don't know," it sighed. "When brains were being handed out, you humans certainly didn't get a bumper amount. Poor things."

Anna wasn't listening. Another wish? If only she didn't feel so sleepy. She knew she'd had the perfect wish planned, but what on earth had it been? All she could think of was the film she and Claire had been watching on the telly.

Maybe that would do?

"Please, fairy-godmother, beautiful as can be," she recited, "will you grant this wish for me?"

The bluebottle busied itself beautifying both back legs.

"Of course I will," it buzzed, "so tell it fast and may this wish not be your last."

"I wish to be a great detective," Anna said loudly. "But . . ." she added, "not starting until tomorrow morning."

"Barking black bears!" buzzed the bluebottle. "You *are* getting fussy. However . . . go back to bed and shut your eyes."

The next thing Anna knew it was morning. She opened her eyes, yawned, and then sat up with a start. She was in a strange room! And she wasn't even in bed! She was lying, fully dressed, on a sofa in a scruffy-looking office!

She suddenly remembered the bluebottle: *she was a great detective*!

There was a battered old desk in the centre of the room. She went over and examined it.

The top drawer held an empty bottle with

"Wicklow Valley Whiskey" written on the label. (Try saying that fast a few times!) The middle one had a pair of bicycle clips, a blob of chewing-gum and five sweet papers. And in the bottom drawer were two notebooks, a telephone directory, a table tennis ball, a magnifying glass and a pencil with a broken point.

The only other thing in the room, apart from the sofa and the desk, was a rickety wooden chair. Anna took the chair over to the desk and sat down on it.

Now what? she thought.

She stared at the door. The top half was made of frosted glass. And there was something written on it:

enryB annA
EVITCETED ETAVIRP
!llams oot ro gib oot esac oN

As she was trying to read this, she heard footsteps outside in the corridor. A shadow appeared behind the glass of the door. Someone knocked.

She took a deep breath. "Come in!" she said.

A boy looking just like Andy Wilson (who sat in front of her in school and had sticking-out ears and bright red hair) walked into the room.

"Hello," he said. "Are you Anna Byrne, the great detective?"

"I am," said Anna. "What is your problem?"

"My name's Pete Murphy," said the boy who looked like Andy Wilson. "And I've lost my hamster."

"Aha!" said Anna. She opened the bottom drawer of her desk and took out one of the notebooks and the pencil. "Tell me about him. Age? Height? Colour of hair? Colour of eyes? What was he wearing? That sort of thing."

"I said my *hamster*," said Pete. "He wasn't wearing anything. Hamsters don't. And he's called Batman and . . ."

"He's called *what*?"

"Batman. And he's only a couple of months old and about four inches long and he's sort of peachy-brown with white splotches and pink eyes."

Anna licked the end of her pencil. It still didn't write. "You don't have a Biro or anything, do you?"

Pete rummaged through his pockets and brought out a fluff-covered Biro. Anna accepted it and blew the fluff off it; great detectives couldn't be choosy.

"Okay," she said, scribbling furiously. "I've got that. Now, when did you last see him?"

"This morning," said Pete. "When I gave him his breakfast. He was all right then."

"And you definitely shut his cage afterwards?"

"Of course I did. Do you think I'm stupid?"

Anna decided not to answer: she didn't want to lose her only client. She stuffed the magnifying glass, the notebook she'd been using, Pete's Biro and, as an afterthought, the table tennis ball, into her pocket and stood up.

"Come on, then. We'd better inspect the scene of the crime."

"We what?" Pete said.

Anna groaned. Being a detective wasn't easy. "Take me to his cage. The thief might have left a clue."

They walked round to Pete's house. The hamster had been kept in Pete's bedroom, in a strong wooden cage with bars along one side, a wheel to exercise on, a ladder on which it could run up and down and a door with a bolt on it. The door was open.

Anna looked carefully at the cage.

"Do you see any clues?" Pete asked.

She examined the bolt through the magnifying glass she had brought from her office.

"Aha!" she said. "There is a smear of peanut butter here! Did you open the door when you were eating a peanut butter sandwich?"

"No," said Pete. "I don't like peanut butter."

"Good," said Anna. She put the magnifying glass back in her pocket. "Come with me."

They found Pete's little sister Karen and her friend Sophie in the kitchen.

Karen was just spreading a piece of toast with peanut butter.

"Aha!" said Anna again. She was getting very good at this, she thought. "Did you have toast and peanut butter for breakfast?"

"Yes," said Karen. "Why?"

"There's your hamster-thief!" Anna told

Pete. She turned back to Karen. "Where have you hidden Batman?"

"I . . . I . . . don't know what you're talking about," stammered Karen, turning scarlet. "I haven't been near him."

"Is that so?" Anna said. She took out her notebook, found a blank page, grabbed Karen's hand and forced her thumb down on to the paper.

"Hey! Let go!" Karen pulled her hand away.

Anna held up the notebook. "Come with me," she said mysteriously.

They followed her back up to Pete's bedroom. Anna compared the smudge of peanut butter on the bolt of the hamster cage with the smudge in her notebook. "They match." She turned to Karen. "You let Batman out. Where is he?"

Karen started to cry. "I didn't mean to," she sniffled. "I only wanted to show him to Sophie."

"Where is he then?" Pete asked.

"We . . . we don't know. He sort of slipped out of my hands and ran under the bed. We hunted and hunted for him and couldn't find him. We did try, honest we did." Karen's voice rose in a wail.

"All right then. No need to panic," said Anna. "I, Anna, the great detective, will find him."

She took out her magnifying glass again and crawled under the bed.

"Aha," she said, a couple of seconds later. A shoe came flying out from under the bed. The others stood back. It was followed by a book, a torch, a pair of scissors, five marbles, three felt pens and an empty crisp packet. Finally Anna herself crawled out.

"Well?" Pete asked. "Did you find Batman?"

Anna held up a piece of black fur. "When did you last see your cat?" she asked.

"Midnight!" Pete turned on his sister. "You mean you let Midnight in here? You horrible, stupid, sneaky *murderer*!"

"Quick," Anna said. "We may still be in time. Where's Midnight?"

"Probably at the bottom of the hot press," Pete said. "She had her kittens in there. Mum only took them away yesterday to find homes for them."

Anna raced out of the bedroom and across the landing to the hot press. She pulled the door open.

Midnight was sitting on an old bathmat on the floor of the hot press. When she saw Anna, she laid back her ears and growled threateningly.

"It's all right, Midnight. Nice pussy," crooned Anna.

Midnight spat at her.

Anna hesitated. She thought she saw a tiny piece of peach-and-white fur sticking out from under Midnight's paws. She had to do something! Batman might still be alive!

She remembered the table tennis ball she'd brought with her from her office. She waved it in front of Midnight and then bounced it on the landing carpet.

Midnight's ears came forwards. Her eyes grew big and round.

Anna rolled the ball along the floor so that it hit the skirting-board of the opposite wall and came back to her. Midnight's tail started to twitch.

Anna rolled the ball back across the floor.

This time Midnight couldn't resist it. She leapt from the hot press, pounced on the ball, sent it flying across the landing, caught it before it reached the other wall, batted it with one paw towards the top of the stairs and then followed it, rolling nose over tail, down into the hall below.

Anna rushed to the hot press. Batman, quite untouched (except that his hair had been plastered flat where Midnight had licked him like one of her kittens) stared up at her, his whiskers quivering, his little red eyes blinking.

She handed him to Pete. "There you are. The Anna Byrne Detective Agency has solved another case."

"I thought Midnight was eating him, there," said Karen, her face still white.

"Not at all," said Anna airily. "It was obvious. Midnight just wanted a kitten to mother because she'd lost hers. So she took Batman instead."

"Thank you, Anna," said Pete. "You really are a great detective."

"Any time," said Anna.

They put Batman back in his cage and went down to the kitchen. The piece of toast which Karen had been spreading with peanut butter was still on the table. Anna realised she was hungry. It must be nearly lunchtime, she thought, and she hadn't had any breakfast.

She picked up the piece of toast. "I shall

take the evidence with me," she said. "Goodbye, everyone."

She was no sooner outside the door and about to put the toast in her mouth, when a bluebottle appeared, as if from nowhere. It hovered over the piecc of toast and then landed right in the middle of it.

"That's beautiful," it said, uncurling its long proboscis (go ahead – look it up!) and slurping peanut butter up through it in a most unlady-like (let alone unfairy-godmother-like) manner. "There's nothing beats a nice bit of peanut butter."

"Fairy-godmother!" Anna whispered.

"Who else?" murmured the bluebottle with its mouth full. "Pardon me!" It burped and put one of its back feet over its mouth. "Had enough?" it added.

"Yes, thanks," said Anna. "Can I go home now?"

"Shut your eyes."

Anna shut her eyes. She heard a voice: it sounded just like her mother's.

"Anna?" the voice shouted, "did you hear

me? It's time to get up. You'll be late for school!"

Anna opened her eyes. She grinned. The first thing she'd do when she got to school would be to ask Andy Wilson how his hamster Batman and his cat Midnight were.

Never in a million years would anyone guess how she knew about them!

Anna's Fourth Wish:
The Zoo

Anna had only three wishes left. She told herself that she had to use them wisely. Fortunately, her fairy-godmother never seemed to be in a hurry to turn up again so she had plenty of time to decide what to wish for next. Or so she thought.

That very same afternoon, when she was in the back garden, collecting leaves for her nature homework, she found a bloated, black, slimy slug oozing its way along the garden path. She stopped with one foot in the air. Should she step over it? Or should she step on to it and squash it flat?

"Don't even think it!" said the slug.

Anna froze, her foot still in the air, looking

like someone caught in a game of musical statues.

"Fairy-godmother!" she whispered. "You're back! I didn't expect you so soon!"

"Surprise me," said the slug. It shrugged, sending a ripple down its black ridged back. "You haven't changed, have you? Still doing your I'm-a-big-human-and-I'll-stamp-on-anything-smaller-than-myself-any-time-I-feel-like-it thing."

"No, I'm not! I *have* changed. I've been extra-specially nice to spiders and flies ever since I met you. And I'd have been nice to mice too, if I'd seen any."

"Huh," sniffed the slug. "Big deal."

Anna decided not to argue. "Please, can we get on with my wish?" she asked as politely as she knew how. "I've got a lot of homework to do."

"You have, have you?" mocked the slug. "Serves you right." Puffing itself up and then stretching itself out, it began to slide slowly round the edge of her shoe, leaving a shining silver trail on the path.

"Hey! Wait a minute!" Anna moved her

foot to block its progress. "Please, fairy-godmother, beautiful as can be, will you grant this wish for me?" she gabbled quickly down at it.

The slug stopped. It seemed to be trying to make up its mind. Then: "I haven't much choice," it grumbled eventually, "do I? Not now that you've said the words. So you might as well tell it fast and may this wish not be your last. Which it will be," it added threateningly, "if you keep being unkind to poor dumb animals."

Anna felt like being *very* unkind to one poor *un*dumb animal, but she controlled herself. "I keep telling you I'm fond of animals," she insisted. "There's nothing I'd like more than to have a zoo of my own. So there."

"Shut your eyes, then," said the slug.

Anna automatically shut her eyes. She opened them again. "But that's not my wish!" she yelled.

She thought she heard a voice say "Tough," but when she looked down the slug had gone.

"Blast!" Anna muttered. "She's obviously gone off in a huff. And she probably won't come back for ages now to give me my next wish. I suppose I'd better get on with my nature project."

She put out a hand to pluck a leaf from the rhododendron bush beside the garden path. A deep growl came from inside the bush. She jumped. Two fierce yellow eyes stared out at her from the darkness behind the leaves. *And then a tiger came out of the bush!* It yawned and stretched itself, looking like a huge cousin of Anna's tabby cat, Tiptoes.

"Mark!" Anna screamed. "*Mark!* He—e—l—p!"

Mark was supposed to be minding her until Mr and Mrs Byrne came home from work, but he was playing with his computer in his bedroom and didn't hear her.

The tiger sidled up to Anna, purring like a wonky bus engine. It looked as if it wanted her to stroke it. She knew better than to stroke a tiger, though. She backed up the path towards the house, not daring to take her eyes off it. "*Nice* tiger!" she murmured to it soothingly. "*Pretty* tiger! *Nice* pussy-cat!"

A hairy orang-outang sprang from the apple tree, grabbed the clothes-line with a long skinny arm and swung towards her, grinning from one sticking-out ear to the other.

As she dodged, her foot hit something which was lying across the path. She looked down.

A crocodile looked up at her with small beady eyes! It smiled, showing teeth which reminded her of one of the posters at her dentist's. Then it waddled across to the goldfish pond and slid into the water.

She took a step back and found herself up against a pillar. Only there weren't any pillars in the garden. She felt behind her: the pillar was covered in dusty leather. She turned round.

An elephant towered up over her! Three of its feet were in the vegetable patch, completely squashing two broccoli plants and six of her father's prize leeks; its fourth leg was the one she'd been leaning up against!

She squealed with fright as a snake slid round her waist.

"Please, fairy-godmother!" she whispered. "Come back! I need you! I want everything to be as it was before!"

The "snake" tightened itself round her waist and then lifted her up into the air. It was the elephant's trunk!

She suddenly found herself sitting on the elephant's neck, just behind the dome at the top of its head. She held on to a large leathery ear to steady herself. It was like being on the warhorse when she'd fought the dragon, only the elephant was even bigger. She looked down.

The garden was full of animals! Apart from the tiger, the orang-outang and the crocodile, there were kangaroos hopping about on the lawn with babies in their pouches, parrots flitting in and out of the raspberry canes, flamingos balancing on one leg in the goldfish pond and a giraffe standing in the middle of the flower-bed, looking as if it were waiting for roses to grow up over it.

If Mrs O'Flaherty from next door should

come out now! Anna thought in alarm. Explaining away a huge ice cream cone was bad enough; how could she explain away a zoo?

Mark finally realised something funny was happening in the garden. He pushed open his bedroom window. "What on earth's going on?" he shouted down to her. "What are you doing on that elephant? How did all these animals get here?"

Anna shrugged. There was no point in trying to explain about her fairy-godmother again; nobody, not even Mark, would believe her.

"Just stay where you are," Mark told her. "I'll be down in a minute."

Anna stayed where she was, on the elephant's back. Well, what would you have done?

A couple of minutes later, Mark came out of the house carrying a large piece of cardboard and a biscuit tin. He turned the cardboard round so that she could see what he'd written on it. "What do you think of that?"

COME TO THE ZOO!
Admission 50p
LIMITED OPENING, SO HURRY –
JUST FOLLOW THE ELEPHANT!!!

"Here," he said, handing it up to her. "You ride round the streets on the elephant with this notice, I'll stand at the gate and collect the 50ps. Okay?"

"But . . ." Anna started.

Mark whacked the elephant on its rump. "Gee up, there!"

The elephant put its trunk into the air, trumpeted loudly and started to amble off towards the back gate. Mark held the gate open, waved it through and shut the gate behind it.

"Wait a minute . . ." shouted Anna, holding on tightly to the elephant's ear.

Neither Mark nor the elephant listened. Mark fetched a garden chair from the shed and set it up beside the gate. The elephant plodded on down the back lane.

They came out into the main road. Realising that she wasn't going to fall off,

Anna relaxed her grip on the elephant's ear and held up Mark's sign.

"A zoo!" people said.

"Wanna go to the zoo!" shouted the children who were old enough to talk.

"Waaa!" yelled the babies in prams and pushchairs.

"Ellie!" screamed the toddlers. "Big ellie!"

The elephant walked proudly on. Anna sat, equally proudly, on its back displaying Mark's poster. She felt like the Pied Piper of Hamelin as children, parents, and curious passers-by formed an excited procession behind her.

Mark was ready at the gate when she got back. He held it open for Anna and the elephant, and then allowed the people in. The pile of 50p pieces in his biscuit tin grew higher and higher. More and more people streamed into the Byrnes' back garden.

"Look, Daddy! A tiger!" shouted a little girl.

The tiger, which had been lying on the patio sunning itself, stood up, yawned (showing sharp yellow teeth) and shook itself, just like Tiptoes waking from her nap.

The crowd went "Ooooh!" and jostled each other to get as far away from it as possible. The people at the back of the crowd found themselves at the edge of the goldfish pond.

The tiger raised its head and gave a roar.

The crowd went "Aaaah!" and the people at the edge of the goldfish pond were pushed *into* the goldfish pond.

"Look, Mummy! A crocodile!" shouted a little boy.

The crocodile opened one eye and winked at Anna.

The crowd went "Ooooh . . . aaaah . . . HELP!" and the people in the goldfish pond leapt back out on to the lawn, pushing those already there back towards the tiger.

There was pandemonium!

Some of the people escaped by scrambling into Mr Kelly's garden. Others climbed the wall into Mrs O'Flaherty's. The rest pushed and shoved, trying to get out of the garden, screaming and yelling in alarm.

Mrs O'Flaherty's door opened at the same time as Mr Kelly's.

"Anna!" yelled Mrs O'Flaherty. "What is going on?"

"Get these people out of my garden!" yelled Mr Kelly, "or I'll call the police!"

"Please, fairy-godmother," Anna whispered. "I want to end my wish!"

She shuddered as she realised that the slug had probably been crushed to death by hundreds of trampling feet. She'd have to do something fast, herself, before somebody got hurt.

She took a deep breath. "Okay, elephant," she whispered into the big ear in front of her. "Go for the gate!"

The elephant seemed to understand. Raising its trunk and adding its loud trumpet to the yells of the people, the screeching of the parrots and the roaring of the tiger, it lumbered towards the gate.

People squeezed themselves out of its way.

Anna ducked as the orang-outang swung out of the plum tree, sailed over her head and landed on the roof of the shed. It looked down at Mark thoughtfully, scratched its armpit and then, stretching out a long hairy arm, it grabbed the biscuit tin with the money and jumped down into the lane.

The elephant stopped, wrapped its trunk round Anna again and, very gently, lifted her off its back and placed her safely on the ground beside Mark. Then it opened the garden gate, trumpeted once more and plodded down the lane after the orang-outang.

Anna and Mark ducked into the shed doorway as the crowd streamed out of the garden behind the elephant. The herd of kangaroos and the giraffe followed. The flamingos and parrots flew overhead in a noisy pink and scarlet cloud. For a moment, the lane was full of people and animals – and then they all turned the corner into the main road and disappeared.

Anna looked back at the house: the tiger had gone and Tiptoes was sitting outside the back door, washing herself.

She turned to Mark. "Are you okay?"

"What happened?" he asked. "Where did all these animals come from? And where have they gone now?"

Those were exactly the questions the police asked Anna and Mark when they arrived a

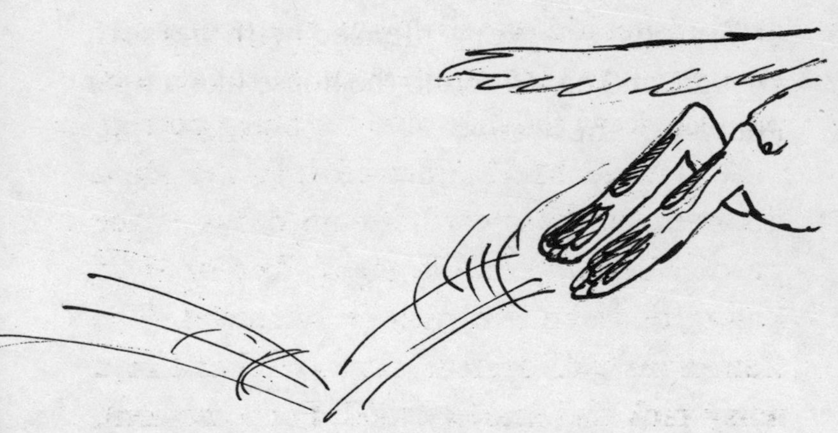

short time later. And the questions Mrs O'Flaherty and Mr Kelly asked anybody they could get hold of for days afterwards.

And "What happened?" is what Mrs Byrne said when she came home from work and saw the state of her garden. She, and later Mr Byrne, said more too, but Anna preferred not to remember that.

"I don't know," Anna told everyone. Well, she didn't *really*, did she? "Some animals must have escaped from a zoo."

And that was what appeared in the papers and on the evening television news.

Strangely enough, the animals were never seen again. And the money that Mark had collected was never found.

Tiptoes was very pleased with herself, though, and paced round the house like a tiger for weeks afterwards.

Anna's Fifth Wish: Pirates

Anna waited impatiently for her fairy-godmother to turn up again.

One morning, when the lawn had been re-laid, the raspberries re-staked and the vegetable patch dug over, she was in the back garden looking for plums. Mark must have been there before her because there were no ripe ones left on the bottom branches of the tree. And the ones which had fallen to the ground had all been nibbled by slugs.

"Nice, *beautiful* slugs," Anna said out loud, just in case her fairy-godmother was around.

She picked up one half-eaten plum and took a bite out of its good side. It was beautifully sweet and juicy! She was just bending to pick up another when a wasp flew out of it.

Anna jumped back with a shriek.

The wasp buzzed round her head and settled on her shoulder. She froze, terrified.

"You're scared stiff, aren't you?" it said with a giggle. "That's nice."

Anna, *very* carefully, turned her head so that she could see it. "Of course I'm scared," she said angrily. "Wasps sting."

"And water turns into ice," said the wasp. "Hic!"

"Sorry?"

"Apology accepted."

"No, I meant: I don't understand."

"So, what's new?" The wasp giggled again.

For the first time since they'd met, Anna realised, her fairy-godmother actually sounded happy. "What has water to do with it?" she asked through gritted teeth.

"Water turns into ice *sometimes*. Wasps sting *sometimes*. But only if you annoy them. *Hic!*" it went again. "Excuse me!" It put one of its six legs politely over its mouth. "Anyway," it added, "as long as people don't move, they're quite safe. We do know how to tell the difference between a human being and a piece of fruit, you know. Fruit's *much* nicer. So, if you stay still we'll get bored and go away. In fact, I'm beginning to get quite bored now. *Hic!*"

"Wait a minute," Anna said. "Please! You

can't go yet. I know exactly what I want this time."

She and Mark had been wishing that they hadn't lost the zoo money. The two of them kept thinking of more and more things they could have spent it on. So she knew just what she was going to ask for and she had prepared each word carefully to make sure that nothing could go wrong.

"I want never gets," quoted the wasp smugly. "Hic! Drat that plum juice!"

Anna wasted no more time. "Please, fairy-godmother, beautiful as can be, will you grant this wish for me?" she recited quickly.

The wasp hiccupped again. It replied even faster than Anna, running the words together so that they came out in an indistinct mumble:

"OkayIwillbuttellitfastandmaythiswishnotbeyourlast. HIC!"

"I wish," Anna said clearly, "to go on an adventure and find buried treasure and I want everything to go back to normal the moment I say so!"

"That's three wishes," grumbled the wasp. "Hic!"

"Not really," Anna said.

"Hmph. We'll see what we can do. Shut your eyes."

When Anna opened her eyes again, she was on a ship. A pirate ship! The wooden deck rose and fell – like one of the rides in a funfair which always made her sick. Huge masts soared up from the deck. Above her head, patched sails flapped across the sun with rhythmic cracking noises, splitting the air into light and shade.

On top of one mast was a black flag. The flag showed a skull above a pair of crossed bones. Near the top of the second mast was a tiny balcony, The crow's-nest, Anna remembered it was called. And someone was standing up there, miles above her head, holding a telescope to his eye.

As she watched, the person in the crow's nest suddenly jumped up and down and waved his arms about. "Land ahoy!" he shouted. "Land ahoy!"

"Heave ho, me hearties! Land ahoy it is!" bellowed a loud voice.

Anna spun round.

Behind her stood a giant of a man with a bushy black beard. A spotted red scarf was tied round his head, a black eyepatch covered one eye, a blue-and-white striped jumper was stretched over his bulging belly, and his cut-off baggy trousers ended in two hairy legs, two unmatched striped socks and two leather slippers with holes in the toes. A parrot, like the ones which had perched in the raspberry canes in her garden, sat on his right shoulder. He must be the pirate captain, Anna thought.

The parrot looked at her. *"Sqwarrrk!"* it said. "Stranger on board! Make her walk the plank!" It tweaked the ring in the pirate's ear.

Fortunately, before the pirate captain could take the parrot's advice, the person in the crow's-nest climbed down the rigging and jumped onto the deck. "Island off the starboard bow, Captain," he reported. Apart from the pigtail hanging down his back, he looked just like Mark.

Well, what did you expect?

Anna wasn't really surprised either. She glanced down at her own clothes: like everyone else on the ship she was wearing a striped T-shirt and ragged trousers. She felt her hair: it, too, was done up in a pigtail.

"Left hand down a bit!" the captain shouted to a sailor holding on to a huge wooden wheel at the back of the ship.

"Aye, aye, sir!" cried the sailor, turning the wheel to the left.

"I said 'starboard'," said the boy who looked like Mark.

"Oh!" said the pirate captain. He turned back to the man at the wheel. "*Right* hand down a bit, you son of an ignorant jellyfish!" he shouted. "Don't you know your left hand from your right?"

"*Sqwarrrk!* Keelhaul him!" squawked the parrot.

The sailor just grinned and turned the wheel the other way.

"Where are we?" Anna asked the captain.

"Just arriving at Treasure Island, boy – I mean, girl. Where else?"

"*Sqwarrrk!* Gold doubloons! Pieces of eight! Luvverly money!" squawked the parrot happily.

Gradually, an island came into view on the horizon. First the top of its palm trees, then the palm trees themselves, then a long white beach.

With a lot of "Left hand down a bit," and "Right hand up a bit," and "Steady as she goes," most of which the man at the wheel just seemed to ignore, the pirate ship finally anchored in front of the sparkling beach.

"All ashore, me hearties!" shouted the captain. "Last one to the beach owes me 5p!"

"Sqwarrrk!" screamed the parrot. "5p! What's wrong with gold doubloons?"

The men shinned over the side of the boat, jumped into the water and started to wade ashore. Anna followed them.

The sea was as warm as bathwater and incredibly blue and clear. She felt like swimming a few strokes, so she did. And she didn't sink, though she always sank in the swimming-pool when her parents took her swimming at home.

Suddenly she heard a lot of yelling and shouting. It was coming from the beach! She put her feet on the sandy bottom and turned to look at the shore.

The pirates were all huddled together on the sand. They looked like a group of little boys cowering in the school yard while some of the bullies from sixth class played football around them. Only it wasn't sixth-class boys who surrounded them. It was half-naked men! And they weren't playing football, they were waving long, pointed spears!

Anna backed closer to the pirate ship.

"Psst!"

She looked round. Was the wasp back, buzzing at her?

"Psst!" someone said again.

The boy from the crow's-nest was leaning over the ship's rail. He put a finger to his lips.

"I'm Tom," he hissed. "Where did you come from?"

"It's a very long story," Anna whispered back. "And you probably wouldn't believe me. What are we going to do about the others?"

They looked across at the sparkling white beach. The natives were herding the pirate crew into the palm-tree grove, like farmers taking sheep to the fair, pigs to the market, *lambs to the slaughter*! Anna shivered. She hadn't been on the ship long enough to get to know any of the crew, and they *were* all pirates, but, even so, when she thought of what might happen to them . . .

"We have to save them," she said.

"Come on, then," said the boy.

He slid down one of the ropes hanging from the side of the ship. Together, they waded through the clear warm water to the deserted beach. Footprints led across the sand and through the palm trees. They followed them.

Beyond the palm trees stood a village of palm-roofed huts. They looked exactly like the holiday villages in the tourist brochures Anna's mother brought home whenever she was feeling depressed by the weather: huts with refrigerators and "kitchenettes," with showers, built-in bars and verandas. (Why shouldn't the natives have a bit of luxury too?)

Anna and Tom crept, *very* carefully, through the palm trees and hid behind one of the huts. Then, even more carefully, they peeked round the side of the hut to see what was going on.

The natives had brought folding chairs into the clearing at the centre of their village, and had arranged them in a circle round the pirates. As Anna and Tom watched, the whole village, mothers, fathers, grandads, grannies, babies, toddlers, teenagers, all sat down on them, just like people taking their seats at a play.

"Now," the native chief said to the pirate captain, "what is it you Irish say at Hallowe'en? Trick or treat!"

"That's right," said the pirate captain. "Only it's not Hallowe'en yet. Hallowe'en's not till October."

The native chief held up a hand to silence him. "Because you came here to trick us of our treasure, you must treat us before we let you go again," he said solemnly. "Sing a song or say a poem or do a dance: we don't mind."

"Oh," said the pirate captain.

The pirates went into a huddle. *"Rhubarb, rhubarb, rhubarb,"* they muttered.

Finally the pirate captain turned to the

audience. "We've decided to do a dance," he announced.

One of the pirates took a tin whistle out of his trouser-pocket. The others stood in a circle, their arms held rigidly down at their sides, their right feet raised in the air, and waited. The pirate with the tin whistle took a deep breath and started to play an Irish reel.

Anna and Tom had to put their hands over their mouths to stop themselves from laughing out loud as the pirates faced each other, spun each other round and jigged in circles and figures of eight, with their bellies bouncing up and down in time to the music and the sweat pouring off their foreheads and soaking into their beards.

"Can we stop now?" begged the captain as the reel came to an end. "I promise we won't steal your treasure. We'll leave now. Cross my heart and hope to die!"

"Not yet," said the native chief. He gestured to the pirate with the tin whistle to start playing again.

As the pirates desperately tried to keep up with the music (they were really *very* unfit for pirates!), Anna whispered to Tom: "I wonder where the treasure's hidden. I only came here because I wanted to find secret treasure. Of course, you wouldn't know where it is," she added craftily. "You're only a cabin boy."

"Huh," said Tom. "That's what you think." He pulled a folded piece of paper from his pocket and waved it in front of her.

Anna grabbed it from him. It was the map of an island! Could it be this island? The beach and the palm trees marked on it looked just like the ones here, and there was a village right in the centre. And, at the far side of the village, someone had drawn a big red X! That must be where the treasure was buried!

She glanced back at the clearing: the pirates were still dancing and the villagers still watching. "Let's go," she said, and started to crawl round behind the huts.

"Come back," Tom whispered. "If they find us, we'll get caught too. And they'll think Captain Jake can't be trusted. He's just promised not to take the treasure."

"I didn't promise," Anna said and kept on crawling. "And anyway, I'm not one of your crew."

"*They* won't know that," Tom said, crawling after her.

"Too bad," said Anna.

They had to push their way through creepers and under vines, with the ground steaming beneath them while, above them, parrots squawked. One of the birds looked suspiciously like the parrot which had once sat on the captain's shoulder.

Finally, they reached the spot marked with an X on the map. A big bush with purple berries stood in front of them.

"Have you got anything to dig with?" asked Anna.

He
Treasu

"No," said Tom. "And anyway, it's stealing."

"The treasure wasn't theirs in the first place," Anna pointed out. "It was just left here. Finders keepers."

"That's rubbish," said the boy. "Finding something that's not your own can't *make* it your own."

Anna stared at him. "You're a weird pirate," she said.

She saw something under the bush. Pushing aside a branch, she found a stick with a notice on it and a plastic spade like the ones you use at the beach.

The notice said:

HERE BE TREASURE!

Excitedly, Anna grabbed the spade and started to dig.

Almost immediately the spade struck something solid.

"Give me a hand!" she urged Tom.

Together they scrabbled at the sand, pulling it away from the object underneath until they finally revealed a small metal chest.

Tom heaved it out of the hole. To Anna's surprise, it wasn't locked.

"Let me open it," she said. "I found it, after all."

Tom hesitated. "Okay," he agreed. "But if there's anything valuable in it we have to give it to charity. That's Pirate's Law."

Anna wasn't listening. She raised the lid of the box . . .

Colours winked up at her: emerald green, golden yellow, ruby red, sapphire blue!

She tipped the treasure out on to the sand, picked up one piece and stared at it.

It was a little green leprechaun with *A present from Ireland; made in the People's Republic of China* stamped on its bottom!

The rest of the treasure was the same. There were more green leprechauns, red Santa Clauses, golden harps, bright blue shillelaghs. All in plastic and all with *Made in the People's Republic of China* on them.

"That's you two for the high jump then!" squawked a familiar voice. "*Sqwarrrk!* A long walk off a short plank, I shouldn't wonder."

Anna looked up. She realised that the music had stopped. She turned round.

She and Tom were surrounded!

"You have broken your word," said the native chief, his voice sounding even sterner than Anna's teacher's had done, the time she'd found Anna reading *Bill's New Frock* in class instead of doing her sums. "You must be killed."

He raised his spear.

Anna dodged. The spear flew past her ear, sounding . . . just like a wasp! She remembered the second part of her wish. Her fairy-godmother hadn't exactly agreed to it, but it was worth a try.

Putting both hands behind her back, she crossed all her fingers. "Please, fairy-godmother," she whispered. "Get me out of here!"

And she was back in the garden. She felt something clenched in her fist. She opened her fingers: it was a little green plastic leprechaun.

Mark was shouting at her. "If you don't come in at once, Mum'll kill you!" he yelled. "Tea's on the table!"

Only one more wish left, Anna thought, as shc trudged back to the house. She'd better make sure she used it wisely.

Anna's Sixth Wish:
Queen Anna

Anna thought long and hard about her last wish. She eventually decided to ask for a million pounds, so that she could buy anything she might ever want to wish for, once her fairy-godmother had gone.

And then she remembered what the pirate boy Tom had said about pirates giving any treasure they found to charity. She wasn't sure that she actually believed him. But . . . Maybe she shouldn't be so greedy. She didn't think her fairy-godmother would like it.

Somehow, she found herself wanting to make her fairy-godmother think well of her. Though why she should want to please someone who was as rude and horrible as her fairy-godmother had been, no matter what shape she had taken, Anna really didn't know.

Was there any way that she could use her final wish to help other people? she wondered.

And then she had an idea. A brilliant idea. She knew just what she was going to do.

Her fairy-godmother returned a few days later. Anna and Mark had built a wigwam out of bamboo canes and an old blanket in the garden. It was probably the last sunny Saturday they'd have before winter, Mr Byrne had said, and they should enjoy it while they could.

Mark had just gone round to the shop to buy some crisps and a couple of cans of Coke. Anna set two mugs on the plank they were using as a table, ready for when he came back. A woodlouse crawled out of one of them.

"Yuck!" Anna yelped. She swept it off the plank and on to the grass.

It lay where it had landed, in an armour-plated ball. Then it uncurled itself and stretched. "There you go again," it complained. "What have you got against woodlice?"

Anna bent down to look at it properly. She was reminded of the time she'd been turned into a knight. She wondered if the dull grey casing that covered its back was as heavy and awkward to the woodlouse as her armour had been to her.

It stood on tiptoes on its three pairs of legs and arched its back. "Have a good stare, why don't you?" it said. "You must admit I'm quite fantastically beautiful. The trouble with you human things is that you never stop to look."

The mouse had been sort of sweet, Anna thought. But the woodlouse was just as ugly as the spider or the slug had been – and slightly scary as well, like a tiny alien monster. Still, maybe it was beautiful, for a woodlouse. Who knows what woodlice like?

"I'm glad you've come back," she said. "This is going to be my last wish, isn't it?"

"Yep," said the woodlouse. "So you'd better make it good, babe."

"Do you mind if I ask you something first?"

"You don't learn, do you?" snorted the woodlouse. "Still trying to sneak in an extra wish."

"No. It's not that. It's . . ." Anna hesitated. How could she say this tactfully? "It's just that I wonderd why, if you're a fairy-godmother and can make magic and everything, why you're always so ru . . . I mean, so *unhappy* yourself."

"Me, unhappy?" The woodlouse turned its back on her and curled up into a ball again. Anna wondered if she had just thrown away her last wish. She hoped she hadn't.

She waited.

Finally, the woodlouse uncurled itself. "Wouldn't you be unhappy," it asked, "if you had to help people, who hate you, to get whatever they want? And if what they want is always something greedy and selfish?" It sighed. "I just get very fed up with it sometimes."

"I'm sorry," Anna said. And this time she really *was* sorry.

"Ah, well," The woodlouse's voice sounded shaky. It couldn't be crying, could it? Anna wondered. Did woodlice cry? "There's not a lot any of us can do about it, I suppose. Humans will be humans, and you can't expect a leopard to change its spots. So we'd better get on with your last wish. After that, we won't need to see each other ever again."

"But . . ." Anna liked the idea of having a fairy-godmother. She didn't want to lose her. "Can't you come back and talk to me sometimes? You don't need to grant me any more wishes."

"*Talk* to you? You have to be kidding!" The woodlouse was back to its normal self. "You've nearly killed me six times now. I'm not going to risk a seventh!"

"I promise I won't harm you." But could she keep that promise? She'd swiped at the woodlouse automatically just a few minutes ago. If she'd killed it, she wouldn't really have worried. "Couldn't you come back as something bigger?" she asked.

"What? Like a sheep or a cow or a pig? Something that you can eat?"

"No, I didn't mean that. Maybe a cat or a dog? I don't know."

"Well, I do. You have one more wish and that's that. Get on with it."

"But . . ."

"No buts. If you haven't wished by the time I've counted to four, you've had it. I'm off. One . . . two . . ."

Anna sighed. "All right, then." She looked down at the woodlouse and said, not at all sarcastically, "Please, fairy-godmother, beautiful as can be, will you grant this wish for me?"

"Of course I will, so tell it fast . . . But remember: this wish *will* be your last. Try to use it well, for a change."

Anna was very pleased with the wish she'd prepared. *"I wish to be queen until I want to be myself again!"*

"What did I say?" asked the woodlouse. "Greedy and selfish as always. And anyway, Ireland's a republic. You can't be queen."

"I'm sure you can fix it," Anna wheedled. "You're brilliant at doing magic."

"Hmph. If you think I don't recognise flattery when I hear it, you have a lot to learn, child. Still, a wish is a wish. So close your eyes."

When Anna opened her eyes again, she was sitting on a golden throne in a high-ceilinged room. The floor was carpeted in white and gold, the golden chairs were covered in red velvet and the high windows, flanked by gold curtains, showed a view of a courtyard with gilded railings. Behind the railings two sentries in fancy uniforms with black furry hats marched up and down.

There was a knock at the door.

"Come in!" she said.

A footman in gold-and-scarlet livery and a white powdered wig came into the room. He bowed. "The Prime Minister is here to see you, Your Majesty."

"Show him in," said Anna.

The Prime Minister came into the room. He too bowed.

"Please sit down," Anna said grandly.

The Prime Minister sat gingerly on the edge of one of the red-and-gold chairs. He looked just like Anna's Dad; he was even wearing the plastic apron Anna and Mark had bought for his last birthday, the one with

Dishwashing Dad, the Fastest Mop in the West! written on it.

"Good morning, Your Majesty," the Prime Minister said. "It's a lovely day, isn't it? I hope you are keeping well. And how are the dogs?"

"We have no time for that this morning," Anna said sternly. "I have decided that there are lots of things to be done and I want them done today."

"But, Your Majesty . . ." stuttered the Prime Minister, his smile slipping. "That's not the way our great constitution works. I tell you what your Government has decided to do and you most royally agree to it all. That's the way it's always been done."

"Well, things have changed," said Anna. "If you don't do what I tell you to, I'll . . . I'll have your head cut off!"

The Prime Minister went white. "You can't do that," he said. "It's unconstitutional!"

"Can't I?" said Anna. "Who's queen here, you or me? Now, have you got a notebook and pencil?"

The Prime Minister, beginning to sweat slightly, felt in the pocket of his apron and took out a crumpled brown envelope with *Top Secret!* stamped across it. "Er . . . will this do, Your Majesty?"

Anna was shocked. If she'd suggested taking notes on the back of a used envelope at school, she knew what Mrs MacRae, her teacher, would have said. Still, she was queen now and could be gracious.

"If you've nothing better," she agreed. "Okay. Number one. I want every school in the country to have ten months' holiday."

"But they're only just back from their summer holidays," stuttered the Prime Minister. "We can't give them holidays again."

Anna ignored him. "Number two. I want sweets and chocolates and crisps and ice cream all to be given away free."

"But . . ."

"You can put up the price of beer and cigarettes if you want. I don't like them." Anna looked at the Prime Minister sharply. "Are you writing this down?"

"Er, yes, Your Majesty," said the Prime Minister, scribbling furiously. "No school for ten months and sweets and chocolate bars and ice cream to be free."

"And crisps," said Anna.

"And crisps," agreed the Prime Minister.

"That's better," Anna said. "Now, what else?" She stared out of the window. A tramp in a tattered raincoat was shuffling past the palace railings. "I don't want anyone in my kingdom . . . I mean, *queendom* to be poor. See that everyone gets a thousand pounds by this afternoon."

"Ev . . . ev . . . everyone? A thou . . . thousand pounds?" spluttered the Prime Minister. "But we haven't got the money!"

"Find it," snapped Anna. "Get it from the bank. Or make some more. And another thing, I want to get rid of the army and the navy and the air force."

"But we can't do that!" shrieked the Prime Minister. "We need them!"

"No, we don't," said Anna. "This will be a peaceable queendom. And, while you're at it, close down all the factories which pollute the air. Okay?"

The Prime Minister smiled craftily. "What about cars and buses, Your Majesty? Do you want us to get rid of them too?"

"No. Why?"

"They pollute just as much as factories." The Prime Minister looked like Anna's Dad did when he was just about to beat her at Scrabble.

"Okay. So get rid of them, too," she ordered.

"How do we do that without causing even more pollution?" the Prime Minister asked, smirking as if he'd just come up with a triple word score with two triple letter scores while using a Z and a Q and an X.

Anna looked at him coolly. "That's your problem," she said. "You're Prime Minister." She stood up to show that the audience was at an end. "You may go now. But make sure you've done everything I said by teatime or I *will* have your head chopped off."

The Prime Minister's smile disappeared. He backed hastily out of the room.

Anna rang the bell for the footman. "Bring round the royal coach!" she ordered. "I wish to see my queendom!"

Five minutes later, she was driving through Dublin in a golden coach pulled by six white horses. People stopped in the streets and waved to her. Anna waved back. It was even better than being on the elephant!

She drove to the sea and dipped her royal toes in the water (it wasn't as warm, or as clear, as that round Treasure Island, but she enjoyed paddling in it all the same) and then she drove back through streets full of cheering people. It was great fun.

Back at the palace she had tea all by herself in a cosy little parlour overlooking the front gate. As she ate her third piece of chocolate cake, she glanced out of the window. A huge crowd was gathering on the pavement outside the palace. They all held newspapers in their hands and were talking excitedly to each other.

Anna rang for a footman and asked him to bring her a paper. The headline was just what she had hoped for.

Queen Anna takes
over government!

Today, by royal command, schools have been closed, sweets and ice cream are free, everyone is to be given a gift of £1,000, cars are to be abolished, factories which pollute the countryside are to be shut down and the Armed Forces disbanded.

She didn't bother to read any more. She was delighted with herself.

"Er . . . Excuse me, Your Majesty." It was the footman back again. "The crowd is becoming restless, Your Majesty. What should we do?"

Anna smiled. "They just want to thank me for making life better for them. Let them come in."

The footman looked doubtful. "Perhaps I should ask the head of the Palace Guards to come in as well? Except . . . oh, dear . . . he's probably been sacked."

"Don't be silly," said Anna. "I am the Queen. My people love me. Open the gates."

She waited for her loyal subjects to come and thank her for her kindness. Her fairy-godmother would be pleased with her this time, she thought smugly. She'd certainly helped to make the world a better place.

The footman stumbled, white-faced, into the room. "I tried to stop them," he stuttered, but was swept aside as a crowd of people surged past him.

Anna stood up. "Good afternoon, ladies and gentlemen," she said in her grandest voice. "How nice of you to call. I'm so glad I could help you all."

Everyone started shouting at once.

Anna blew a loud whistle on her fingers, a trick Mark had taught her when she was four. Everyone shut up in amazement.

"Now, then," she said, trying to sound like Mrs MacRae, last period on a rainy Friday afternoon when things were starting to get out of control in the classroom. "I can't hear you if you all talk at once. One at a time, please. Just put up your hands . . . yes. The tall man with the moustache. You wanted to thank me?"

"*Thank* you?" snorted the tall man with the

moustache. "I'm a dentist. Do you know what your new law about sweets and chocolates will do to children's teeth?"

"And I'm a shopkeeper," shouted a little fat lady in corduroy jeans. "I'll go broke if I have to give away sweets and ice cream for nothing."

"And I'm a parent!" shouted a man with curly brown hair. "I want my kids educated! If there's no school for another ten months, how are they to learn anything?"

"I agree," said a pretty lady in a purple dress. "I'm a teacher, and we need all the time we can get with the children. They have far too many holidays already!"

"That's not important," shouted an elderly woman. "I work in a factory. If all the factories are going to close, what about my job?"

"And mine!" shouted a young man. "I make motor-cars. You've just done away with them."

"You'll get a thousand pounds," Anna said quickly.

"A thousand pounds?" sneered the young man. "That won't go far with a wife, three kids, a dog and a mortgage to support."

"And it won't help the unemployed," shouted the tramp in the tattered raincoat whom she'd seen shuffling past the place earlier. "We need *jobs*, not handouts."

"And what about us?" shouted a group of men and women in uniform at the back of the crowd. "Do you want us all out of work, too? There are thousands and thousands of us in the army and navy and air force."

Anna was horrified. "I was only trying to help. I thought you'd be pleased."

"Pleased?" shouted the crowd. It started to move forwards. The people behind were

pushing the people in front. Angry faces came nearer and nearer.

Anna took a step back. Then another. She felt the wall behind her, and still the crowd came on.

"Ok," she whispered. "What would you all like?"

"The Queen wants to know what you would like!" proclaimed the footman.

"Riches!" "Health!" "Happiness!" "Love!" shouted the crowd.

Anna heard a familiar voice coming from down by her feet. "A fine mess you've got yourself into this time," it said.

"Phew," Anna said. (You didn't think anyone ever said "phew," did you? Maybe Anna read Enid Blyton too.) "Fairy-godmother! Thank goodness you're here!"

She looked down: the woodlouse was sitting on the skirting-board. "Can't we do anything?" she whispered to it.

"Like what?"

"I don't know. Change people's minds, so that they don't fight and pollute and aren't so greedy?"

"Too hard," said the woodlouse.

"Well, *something!*" said Anna.

"Bend down a minute," said the woodlouse.

Anna bent down and listened while the woodlouse whispered into her ear. She looked doubtful. "I don't know," she said, straightening up again.

And then she had an idea. Not a brilliant idea, perhaps, but one which wouldn't cost anyone their job and which might, just maybe, make the world a happier place. She turned to face the crowd of angry people.

"All right," she said. "I made a mistake. I hereby get rid of all the laws I made today – apart from the one about pollution. Cars and factories don't have to pollute so much. And I'm going to give you just one royal command which you all have to obey. Okay?"

The crowd waited suspiciously.

"Everyone," Anna declared, "has to smile at someone else *at least once every day.*"

The crowd looked at each other in surprise. A few people scratched their heads. Some tried a tentative grin.

"You all have to start *now*," Anna told them firmly.

More and more people started to smile at one another. Some even laughed. Soon the whole room was smiling and laughing.

Anna turned to the woodlouse. "Can we go now?" she asked.

"Shut your eyes, then," the woodlouse said.

When Anna opened her eyes again, she was back in the wigwam and Mark was dumping crisps and a can of coke on the grass beside her. "You'd better pay me back when you get your pocket money," he told her.

Anna wished she had used her last wish to ask for a million pounds, after all. She looked through the wigwam door into the garden. A wasp settled on the fence for a few seconds and then flew off again, passing a spider sitting by its web. A bluebottle buzzed nearer and nearer to the web, as if laughing at the spider, and then disappeared over the raspberry canes (where the wasp was now adding bits to its paper nest in a corner of the wall). On the garden path, a slug and a

woodlouse appeared to be having a race. And could she see the bright eyes of a mouse, peeking out from under the garden shed?

She thought of going round the garden, trying to get even *one* of them to talk to her, no matter how much of an idiot she looked to Mark. But she knew it would be no use. She'd had her last wish and that was that. No more magic. And she'd wasted most of her wishes. She had nothing to show for them apart from the few cartons of ice cream which were left in the freezer; and they'd soon be gone, too.

She'd even lost the plastic leprechaun somewhere.

But it had been fun while it lasted.

"Goodbye, fairy-godmother," she whispered into the garden when Mark's back was turned. "And thanks."

two chimneys appeared to be having a race; and could she see the [illegible] eyes of [illegible] peeking out from under the garden shed?

She thought of going round the [illegible] [illegible] to see [illegible] [illegible] no matter how [illegible] [illegible] she [illegible]

'And [illegible] she knew it wouldn't [illegible] She'd had her last [illegible] [illegible] [illegible] [illegible] [illegible] [illegible] [illegible] [illegible] [illegible] [illegible] [illegible] [illegible] [illegible] [illegible] [illegible] [illegible] [illegible] [illegible] gone.'

[illegible]

[illegible]

[illegible]

If you had a fairy-godmother, what would YOU wish for?

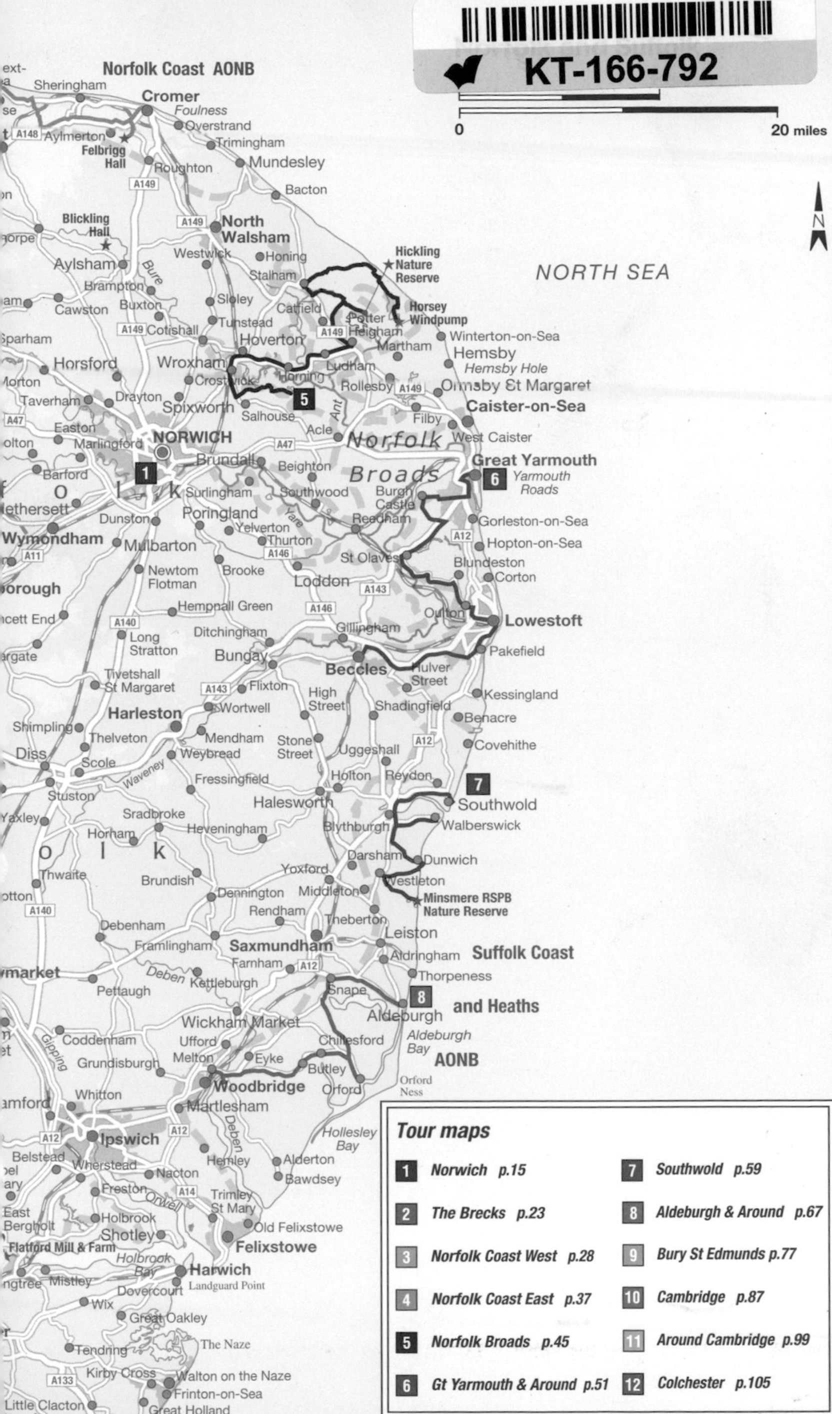
KT-166-792
0
20 miles
N
NORTH SEA
Norfolk Coast AONB
Sheringham
Cromer
Foulness
Overstrand
Trimingham
Aylmerton
A148
Felbrigg Hall
Roughton
Mundesley
A149
Bacton
Blickling Hall
North Walsham
Aylsham
Bure
Westwick
Honing
Stalham
Hickling Nature Reserve
Brampton
Cawston
Buxton
Sloley
Catfield
Horsey Windpump
Potter Heigham
Coltishall
Tunstead
Sparham
Hoveton
Martham
Winterton-on-Sea
Horsford
Wroxham
Ludham
Hemsby
Hemsby Hole
Morton
Crostwick
Horning
Rollesby
Ormsby St Margaret
Taverham
Drayton
Spixworth
5
Salhouse
Ant
Caister-on-Sea
Filby
A47
Easton
Acle
Norfolk
West Caister
Marlingford
NORWICH
Brundall
Broads
Great Yarmouth
1
Beighton
6
Yarmouth Roads
Barford
Surlingham
Southwood
Burgh Castle
Hethersett
Dunston
Poringland
Yare
Reedham
Gorleston-on-Sea
Wymondham
Mulbarton
Yelverton
Thurton
A12
Hopton-on-Sea
A11
A146
St Olaves
Blundeston
Newton Flotman
Brooke
Corton
Loddon
A143
Hempnall Green
A146
Oulton
Lowestoft
A140
Long Stratton
Ditchingham
Gillingham
Pakefield
Bungay
Beccles
Hulver Street
Tivetshall St Margaret
Flixton
High Street
Kessingland
Wortwell
Shadingfield
Harleston
Benacre
Shimpling
Thelveton
Mendham
Stone Street
A12
Covehithe
Diss
Weybread
Uggeshall
Scole
Waveney
Fressingfield
Holton
Reydon
7
Stuston
Halesworth
Southwold
Yaxley
Sradbroke
Blythburgh
Walberswick
Horham
Heveningham
Darsham
Dunwich
Thwaite
Yoxford
Westleton
Brundish
Dennington
Middleton
Minsmere RSPB Nature Reserve
A140
Rendham
Theberton
Debenham
Leiston
Framlingham
Saxmundham
Suffolk Coast
Aldringham
Farnham
A12
Thorpeness
Deben
Kettleburgh
Pettaugh
Snape
8
and Heaths
Aldeburgh
Wickham Market
Coddenham
Ufford
Chillesford
Aldeburgh Bay
Gipping
Melton
Eyke
AONB
Grundisburgh
Butley
Woodbridge
Orford
Orford Ness
Whitton
Martlesham
Ipswich
A12
Hollesley Bay
Belstead
Wherstead
Hemley
Alderton
Nacton
Bawdsey
Freston
Orwell
A14
Trimley St Mary
East Bergholt
Holbrook
Old Felixstowe
Shotley
Felixstowe
Flatford Mill & Farm
Holbrook Bay
Harwich
Mistley
Landguard Point
Dovercourt
Wix
Great Oakley
The Naze
Tendring
Kirby Cross
Walton on the Naze
A133
Frinton-on-Sea
Little Clacton
Great Holland
Tour maps
1 Norwich p.15
2 The Brecks p.23
3 Norfolk Coast West p.28
4 Norfolk Coast East p.37
5 Norfolk Broads p.45
6 Gt Yarmouth & Around p.51
7 Southwold p.59
8 Aldeburgh & Around p.67
9 Bury St Edmunds p.77
10 Cambridge p.87
11 Around Cambridge p.99
12 Colchester p.105

INSIGHT GUIDES

Great Breaks

NORFOLK & SUFFOLK

Contents

Walks and Tours

Travel Tips

Norfolk and Suffolk's Top 10

The high spots of this fascinating and picturesque region cater for all tastes, whether you're a beach fan, bird-spotter, boat enthusiast or culture vulture

▲ **Boating on the Norfolk Broads** *(p.43)*. Hire a boat for the day, take a cruise trip or ideally paddle your own canoe on the delightful waterways of the Norfolk Broads.

▲ **Sutton Hoo** *(p.71)*. You don't have to be an archaeological buff to enjoy this fascinating site of an Anglo-Saxon burial ship, discovered in 1939.

▲ **Ely Cathedral** *(p.98)*. Make a detour to this magnificent Norman cathedral that towers above the flat landscape of the Fens.

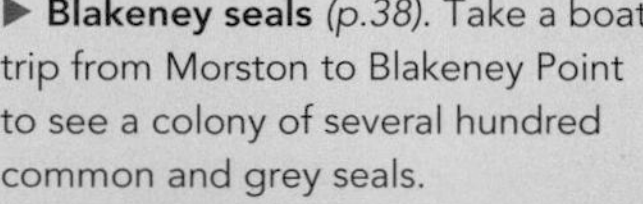

▶ **Blakeney seals** *(p.38)*. Take a boat trip from Morston to Blakeney Point to see a colony of several hundred common and grey seals.

▲ **Cambridge** *(p.85)*. Hop across the county border to see the fine colleges of this celebrated seat of learning.

▲ **BeWILDerwood** *(p.45)*. Take the kids to this magical eco-friendly playground with tree houses and zipwires and meet the forest folk who live deep in the woods.

▲ **Holkham Hall** *(p.34)*. All part of the Holkham estate are the grand Holkham Hall, extensive parklands, nature reserve and the glorious Holkham bay, with miles of unspoilt golden sands.

▼ **Southwold Pier** *(p.59)*. This quirky pier is one of the best in the country, and one of the few along the coast to have survived the storms.

▼ **Minsmere RSPB Nature Reserve** *(p.64)*. Seek out birds and other wildlife at this expertly-run nature reserve, known for marsh harriers and avocets.

▼ **Norwich Cathedral** *(p.18)*. Norwich has many medieval buildings but the magnificent Cathedral, with its soaring spire, is the jewel in the crown.

Overview

Rural Retreat

Big skies, beaches, boating and birding make Norfolk and Suffolk a haven for outdoor enthusiasists, but they also offer historic churches, fine dining and cosy pubs

It is hard to believe, when driving through the empty landscapes and sleepy villages of Suffolk and Norfolk, that East Anglia in medieval times was one of the most densely populated and commercialised regions of England. The broad acres of chalk and grassland provided ideal grazing for sheep, and huge quantities of wool were exported, boosted by the arrival of expert Flemish weavers in the mid-14th century. The main legacy of this era of wealth and prosperity is the region's medieval churches – more than 1,000 of them. It is largely thanks to the region's location, separated from the main north–south axis through Britain, that it has managed to preserve its distinctive architecture, as well as time-honoured traditions and rural character.

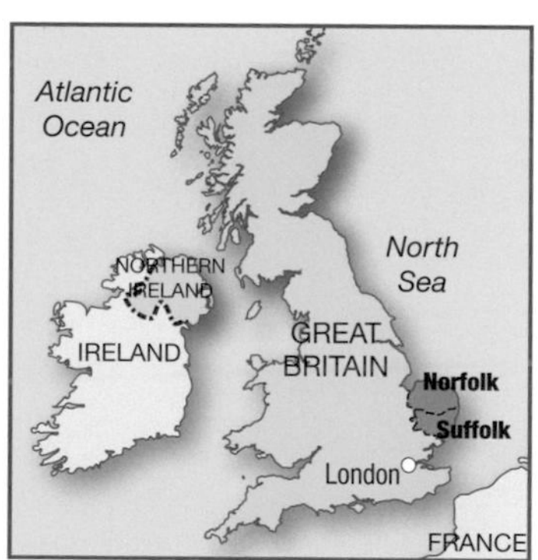

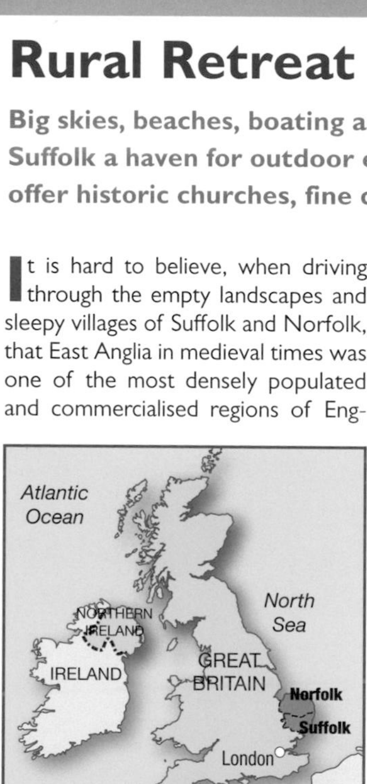

GEOGRAPHY

This is the most easterly region of England, bulging out between the shallow Wash to the north and the River

Stour to the south. Characterised by vast skies and hazy, low horizons, the landscape is flat or gently rolling, with shallow valleys and slow-flowing rivers. The region as a whole incorporates some very distinctive areas. The popular Norfolk Broads are a network of navigable rivers and open lakes which were formed by the flooding of shallow pits made by medieval peat diggers. In western Norfolk the sandy heaths of The Brecks were covered in dense woodland until Neolithic man, using axes made from the flint pits at Grimes Graves, cleared the forest for farming. Bordering the Brecks the haunting flat Fenland is one of the richest arable areas of England, but before the 17th century, when the Dutch masterminded the drainage of the fens, this area was marshland, inhabited by fishermen and wildfowlers.

The magnificent coastline provides diverse seascapes, from multicoloured cliffs and golden swathes of sands to wild marshland, tidal creeks and mudflats. Many of the harbours have silted

Above: horses in a field at sunrise, near Dunwich Heath. **Below**: the river by the Pakenham Watermill, Suffolk.

Above: a sign in Southwold depicting the Battle of Solebay (1672) between the English and the Dutch.

up over the centuries and where there were once thriving ports there are now coastal villages, with just a handful of fishermen.

WHEN TO GO

The region has its attractions all year round. It is the driest part of the UK, and ideal for walking or cycling at any time. The warm summer months attract the most visitors, especially to the coast, but even in mid-summer you should be prepared for northerly and easterly winds from the North Sea. May, June, early July and early autumn are good times to go, while the latter part of July and August are invariably the most crowded, particularly along the coasts. Autumn and winter are great times for walking, and especially for bird-life. Thousands of pink-footed geese migrate from Iceland and Greenland, flying inland at dawn to feast on arable farmland. Coasts provide bracing walks off-season, and winter is the best time to see seals on the beach. At the end of the day there is always a cosy pub nearby with local ale and log fire roaring.

TOURISM

Although agriculture and fishing still have a role to play, the economy increasingly relies on tourism. The great outdoors is the main attraction, with walking, touring, visiting beaches and exploring villages the most popular activities. The extensive waterways of the Broads are among the top attractions, both for boating and for rare wildlife. To the east lies exuberant Great Yarmouth, to the north a coast of huge sandy beaches, well-established English seaside resorts such as Cromer and Sheringham, and tiny coastal villages backing on to wildlife-rich creeks and marshes. The Suffolk coast attracts an arty crowd, particularly Aldeburgh with its famous music festival and little Walberswick with its artistic traditions. Inland Suffolk has some idyllic villages, with quaint timber-framed houses, immaculate village greens and vast flint-faced churches.

In addition to great medieval churches the cultural legacy survives in its Norman keeps, relics of medieval castles, abbeys and monasteries and – from a later era – its magnificent country mansions. Both counties have a vibrant cultural scene with festivals, museums, galleries and arts events. For sightseers the finest towns in the region are Norwich, King's Lynn, Bury St Edmunds and Cambridge (we've crossed over the county border for this unmissable city).

The most notable change in the region in recent years has been the food scene. Pubs, restaurants and cafés have gone from strength to strength, a remarkable number now sourcing high quality produce from local suppliers. Fashionable delis have taken the place of dusty grocers and Michelin rosettes can be found even on the north Norfolk coast. It's no wonder well-heeled Londoners have been snapping up so many properties here. In desirable spots like Burnham Market or Southwold over half the houses are now second homes.

COASTAL ENVIRONMENT

For centuries the coastline has faced an ongoing battle with coastal erosion. In the case of Dunwich an entire port was lost to the sea in medieval times. More recently the coast bore the full force of the wild weather in 1953, with the loss of 307 lives in Norfolk, Suffolk, Essex and Lincolnshire. As a consequence storm surge barriers were constructed on the River Thames and coastal defences were strengthened at high-profile resorts and villages. Others have suffered from recent tidal surges. Hemsby in Norfolk lost five houses to the sea in the tidal surge of December 2013 and the locals are now fundraising and building their own sea defences. This was the worst storm surge since the 1953 floods, with ferocious waves battering seaside towns and villages and breaching coastal defences. It will take some time for the flooded areas, including the damaged nature reserves, to recover. The average loss to the sea is a yard a year, and however great the efforts to protect it, the loss of further coastline is inevitable.

Guide to Coloured Boxes

- E Eating
- F Fact
- G Green
- K Kids
- S Shopping
- V View

This guide is dotted with coloured boxes providing additional practical and cultural information to make the most of your visit. Here is a guide to the coding system.

G Go Green

The Green Traveller Guide (www.greentraveller.co.uk) gives you the low-down on all things green: staying in yurts, farmers' markets, visiting National Parks, Areas of Outstanding Natural Beauty and other protected landscapes. Find out about the greenest accommodation, from camping and country cottages to chic hotels, best pubs and restaurants with locally-sourced food and ales, and details of low-impact activities such as walking, cycling, sailing and kayaking.

Above: view over Dunwich Heath and the Suffolk coastline.

Food and Drink

The last quarter century has seen a transformation of the food and drink scene in Norfolk and Suffolk, thanks to the demand for specialist local producers and the more discerning tastes of holidaymakers.

Thanks to its climate, rich soil and diverse coastline, East Anglia lives up to its reputation as 'the breadbasket of Britain'. Both Norfolk and Suffolk have a field-to-fork philosophy, ie the idea that food can make its way from the ground to your plate without leaving the county. An encouraging number of gastropubs and restaurants put this philosophy into practice, their menus featuring local fare, whether it's ox cheeks from Bramfield, pork from Blythburth, venison from the Suffolk Denholm estate, crab from Cromer or oysters from Brancaster. Menus often inform you exactly where the produce is sourced. A prime example is The Bildeston Crown, Bildeston, whose Red Poll beef, Suffolk lamb and many of the vegetables they serve come from their own farm. Or the British Larder, Woodbridge, whose owners are so dedicated to local fare they operate a 'Barter at the British Larder' system: if you bring them produce from your garden or allotment, they'll turn it into something delicious for you.

It's not just the food that's local. The chances are that your choice of restaurant or pub will be serving real ales and beers from one of the many micro-breweries. The long-established Adnams in Southwold supplies establishments throughout East Anglia – and well beyond – while Norfolk, which claims to have the best malting barley in the country, has more micro-breweries than any other county in the UK.

Many of Suffolk and Norfolk's ancient market towns hold a weekly or monthly farmers' market selling locally-made cheeses, artisan bread, ready-to-cook wild game, and fresh fish and seafood. Among the best are Snape Maltings, Bury St Edmunds, Lavenham, Sudbury and Creake Abbey.

FRUITS OF THE SEA

The fishing scene is not what it was. Lowestoft no longer has a fishing fleet

Above: Cromer crab and fish stall in Great Yarmouth.

Eating Out Price Guide

Two-course meal for one person, including a glass of wine.

£££	over £30
££	£20–30
£	under £20

and the silting up of harbours on the North Norfolk coast led to the decline of formerly thriving fishing ports. But crab-catching still goes on in Cromer, mussels are harvested at Brancaster and oysters come from the creeks around Orford. Samphire, otherwise known as 'sea asparagus' thrives in the north Norfolk salt marshes. At Aldeburgh fishermen still land skate, seabass and Dover sole, selling it from shacks on the shingle beach. Stiffkey on the north Norfolk coast is traditionally famous for cockles, known as Stewkey Blues on account of their distinctive grey-blue shells. The cockles are harvested with broad rakes and nets, then steamed or put in soups and pies.

The sweet tender Cromer crab is justly famous. These small crustaceans thrive on the chalk reef just off Cromer. No one knows exactly why they're so good (they are the same species as other British crabs) but it is generally thought to be the slow speed with which they grow. Crabbing boats, of which there are now only around a dozen at Cromer, go out to lay pots about three miles offshore from March to October. Try the dressed crab at Davies Fish Shop in Garden Street, Cromer. The legendary Davies family go back four generations as lifeboatmen and fishermen. They have their own boat and you can be assured their seafood is as fresh as you'll get.

ALDEBURGH FOOD AND DRINK FESTIVAL

An increasing number of food festivals are taking place but there is none to match Aldeburgh's which is a two-day extravaganza in the halls and marquees of Snape Maltings, celebrating the quality and bountiful harvest of the East Suffolk countryside. This is where you can rub shoulders with well known chefs, meet butchers, bakers and farmers showcasing their produce, attend bread-making sessions, go foraging for nuts and mushrooms, or join a tutored wine tasting session. The event then spreads through the region with farm walks, tastings and workshops across the county for the following fortnight.

E Delis and Farmshops

SUFFOLK

Emmett's, Peasenhall (www.emmettsham.co.uk). Suffolk hams and bacon made the traditional way since 1820.

Lawson's Delicatessen, Aldeburgh (www.lawsonsdelicatessen.co.uk). Award-winning deli.

Suffolk Food Hall, Wherstead, near Ipswich (www.suffolkfoodhall.co.uk). Butcher's, deli, fishmonger, bakery and more all under one roof.

NORFOLK

Elveden Estate, Elveden (www.elveden.com). Home-made produce, butcher's and deli.

Farm to Fork and Fish, Horstead (www.farmtoforkandfish.co.uk). Fresh, seasonal and local produce.

The Galley, 43 Lower Street, Horning (tel: 01692-650 088). Family-run deli, café and gift shop.

Above: fresh fruit and veg at a farmshop in Cley-next-the-Sea.

Tour I

Norwich

Take a step back in time and explore Norwich, an underrated city packed with historical sites and lovely little alleys. This is a full-day 2-mile (3km) walking tour

Until the industrial revolution Norwich was one of the most prosperous cities in England. Set amid rich agricultural land it rose to prominence in the Middle Ages as a market and trading centre, growing rich on its trade of worsted cloth. Tradition has it that the city had a pub for each day of the year and a church for every Sunday. There were in fact 700 pubs in medieval times, down to around 140 today. Evidence of its former prosperity can be seen in the 32 medieval churches and many historic houses dotted around the city.

Norwich also has a large and colourful market, some great little shops, no shortage of excellent cafés and restaurants and a pleasantly relaxed atmosphere.

Highlights

- Norwich Castle Museum
- Norwich Lanes
- Museum of Norwich
- Elm Hill
- Norwich Cathedral
- Sainsbury Centre for Visual Arts

NORWICH CASTLE

The city's gaunt **Castle** ❶ stands high up on a grassy mound above the city centre. It was built as a royal palace but became the county gaol in 1220 and remained so for 650 years until it was bought by the city for conversion to a museum. The Keep, which is all that remains of the original castle, was refaced in 1834 – hence the newer-than-Norman look. The battlements and dungeons can be visited on guided tours (additional charge).

Castle Museum and Art Gallery

Converted from the old prison blocks, the excellent **Castle Museum and Art Gallery** (tel: 01603-493 625; www.museums.norfolk.gov.uk; July–Sept Mon–Sat 10am–5pm, Sun 1–5pm, Oct–June Mon–Sat 10am–4.30pm, Sun 1–4.30pm) offers a combination of fine art, natural history, archaeology and history. The remarkable array of galleries covers everything from Egyptian and Viking history to the world's largest collection of ceramic teapots. The highlight is the art gallery, with an outstanding collection of paintings by the Norwich School (1803–33), a group of landscape painters who drew their inspiration from the Norfolk scenery. The leading figures were John Crome and John Sell Cotman.

THE ROYAL ARCADE

At the castle exit turn right, then right again down the steps, crossing the main road for the **Royal Arcade** ❷ a beautiful Art Nouveau thoroughfare. At No. 15 on the left you'll find **Colman's Mustard Shop and Museum** (tel: 01603-627 889; www.mustardshopnorwich.co.uk; Mon–Sat 10am–4pm, Sun 11am–4pm; free). Farmers in East Anglia have been growing mustard for Colman's for over 180 years, and this specialist shop-cum-museum sells a remarkable range of mustard products as well as souvenirs.

Preceding Pages: Oxburgh Hall. **Left**: Market Place and Norwich Castle. **Above**: the Royal Arcade.

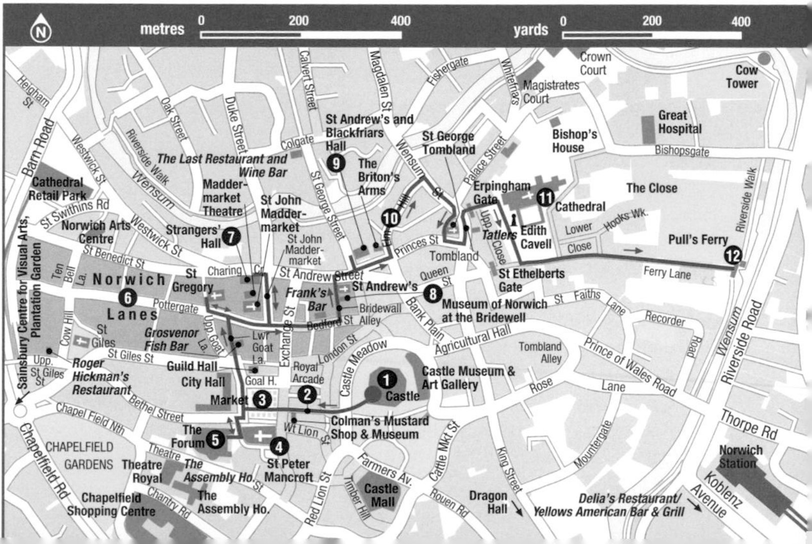

E Delia

Britain's most trusty celebrity chef, Delia Smith, taught the nation to cook during her illustrious 40-year television career. Her books have sold over 21 million copies worldwide – more than any other chef. Delia's other great passion is football. She and her husband have a joint majority shareholding in Norwich City Football Club and are credited with saving the club from bankruptcy in 1996. Football supporters (and others) can enjoy dishes cooked to Delia's high standards at her two Football Club restaurants *(see p.21)*.

MARKET PLACE

At the end of the arcade you come to the **Market** ❸ (Mon–Sat 8.30am–5.30pm), which has been held here for over 900 years. It is one of the largest open markets in Britain, with over 190 tightly-packed stalls selling everything from flowers, fresh cockles and Cromer crabs to cheap clothes and household goods. Food options are abundant: fish and chips, kebabs, take-away Thai food, mushy peas or stuffed Cromer crabs.

On the far side, looms the massive **City Hall** (1938) with its soaring tower; to the right is the 15th-century **Guildhall**, a fine example of the flintwork for which the city is famous, and to the left, with its tower dominating the city centre, the large perpendicular **Church of St Peter Mancroft** ❹ (Mon–Sat 10am–4pm, winter until 1pm, Sun during services only; free). The finest of the city's medieval churches, it has a light and lofty interior with a hammerbeam roof and notable stained glass in the east window depicting the lives of the saints and scenes from the New Testament.

THE FORUM

In stark contrast to the church is the modern glass-fronted **Forum** ❺ (www.theforumnorwich.co.uk) right opposite, built on the site of the old Norwich Central Library which burnt down in 1995. This horseshoe-shaped building encompasses the regional library, the tourist office, BBC East offices, Fusion (a digital screen gallery), as well as shops and a café. Inevitably controversial when it was built in the heart of the historic city, the Forum has nevertheless become a buzzing centre where people meet or gather in the outdoor plaza to watch amateur performances or free screenings of major sporting events and cinema classics. In winter it's a popular spot for ice skating.

POTTERGATE

Cross the square and take Lower Goat Lane behind the Guild Hall, which takes you down to Pottergate. The alleys here and to the east, across Exchange Street, are known as the **Norwich Lanes** ❻, a lively shopping area with enticing little independent outlets and cafés within lovely old

Above: alley leading to the Church of St John Maddermarket.

Above: artifacts at the Museum of Norwich at the Bridewell.

buildings. Turn left at Pottergate and cross into the small square with the flint-faced **Church of St Gregory,** which has a medieval wall painting of St George and the Dragon in the north aisle. About half of the city's medieval churches are no longer used for regular worship but are beautiful buildings at the heart of the city, and many can still be visited by the public. The Norwich Historic Churches Trust cares for 18 of the churches and most of them have been put to good use. St Gregory's, for example, is leased out as a centre for collectables, with around 30 traders.

Returning to Pottergate, turn left to the flint rubble **Church of St John Maddermarket**, named after the red dye of the madder plant used by the local weavers. A passage under the church tower leads to the Maddermarket Theatre, built in Elizabethan style at the end of the 18th century. The Maddermarket leads up to Charing Cross. Turn left for **Strangers' Hall** 7 (tel: 01603-667 229; June–Sept Wed–Sat 10am–4pm, Oct–May Wed and Sat 10am–4pm). This intriguing Tudor house, one of the oldest in Norwich, was once home to wealthy merchants and mayors of Norwich. There are nooks and crannies to explore and rooms in styles varying from medieval to Victorian.

Retrace your steps to Pottergate, turning left along Lobster Lane, then cross Exchange Street for Bedford Street. Many of the houses here date back to the 17th century.

MUSEUM OF NORWICH

Turn left into Bridewell Alley for the **Museum of Norwich at the Bridewell** 8 (tel: 01603-493 625; www.museums.norfolk.gov.uk; Tue–Sat 10am–4.30pm; last admission half an hour before closing). The house was a former bridewell, or prison for petty criminals. In the 19th century it became a tobacco factory, later a leather warehouse and finally a shoe factory, making it a fitting setting for a museum devoted to local industries and crafts. Ten galleries chart the history of the city, with plenty of hands-on fun, archive films and recording. Displays show Norwich in its heyday, when it was England's second city. The city's wealth rested on the production and export of elaborate

Getting There

The city of Norwich has direct rail links with London and Cambridge; the station is less than 10 minutes' walk from the centre. If you are coming by car there are six Park and Ride routes. Alternatively, Castle Mall is the closest car park to the castle where the walk begins, but St Andrew's is cheaper. The Discover Norwich app, available free on iOs and Android, has an interactive map and useful listings.

Ⓢ Retail Therapy

Norwich is a great place to shop, whether it's gifts from the Colman's Mustard Shop in the Royal Arcade, Cromer crabs from the market, vintage clothes from the Norwich Lanes or fashions or homeware from the award-winning Jarrolds department store. For a treasure trove of Eastern delights check out Country & Eastern (www.countryandeastern.co.uk) at 34–36 Bethel Street, next to the Forum. Oriental rugs, kelims, statues and ceramics are laid out in the splendid setting of a former Victorian skating rink.

woven fabrics, used for clothing and furnishing. Shoes replaced weaving as the main industry from 1860 and at its peak there were 26 shoe factories employing 26,000 people. On display are elegant examples of footware, including a thigh-high boot designed for nurses serving in World War II to protect them from snakes and leeches in the Burmese jungle.

ST ANDREW'S TO ELM HILL

Follow the alley for **St Andrew's**, a large medieval church with a stained glass image of Death dancing with a Bishop and fine Renaissance tombs commemorating the Norfolk Suckling family. Cross St Andrew's street for **St Andrew's and Blackfriars Hall** ❾ which together once formed the Dominican Blackfriars convent church. The lofty interior of St Andrew's Hall, whose walls are hung with 127 portraits of former mayors of Norwich, nowadays makes a fine setting for concerts, craft fairs and other events.

Exiting the Hall, turn left up Princes Street and left again for the steeply-sloping **Elm Hill** ❿, the city's medieval showpiece. Originally the home of wealthy merchants, the narrow cobbled street is flanked by beautifully-preserved 16th- to 18th-century houses. **The Briton's Arms** on the corner is one of the few remaining timber-framed thatched buildings to survive in the city and dates back even further.

Turn right at the end of Elm Hill, up to **Tombland**, the former Saxon market place. To the right, opposite the entrance to the cathedral, lies the quaint Tombland Alley with the 16th-century Steward House on the corner. Take the alley, turning left at the end past the parish Church of St George Tombland. Cross the main street for the cathedral.

NORWICH CATHEDRAL

A stunning example of Romanesque architecture, **Norwich Cathedral** ⓫ (tel: 01603-218 300; www.cathedral.org.uk; daily 7.30am–6pm; free but donations welcome; free guided tours Mon–Sat 11am and 3pm; evensong Mon–Fri 5.30pm) is a dominant landmark of the city, its 315ft (96-metre) spire the tallest in Britain after Salisbury's. The core of flints and mortar

Above: houses and shopfronts on Elm Hill.

Above: the spectacular vaulting and arches inside Norwich Cathedral.

came from East Anglia, but the pale stone of the exterior was shipped all the way from Caen in Normandy. The sheer size and grandeur of the building is best appreciated from the south side (which you'll see on exiting).

To the right of the cathedral entrance is a **memorial to Edith Cavell**, the Norwich-born nurse who was executed by the Germans for helping prisoners-of-war escape from Belgium during World War I. After the war her body was brought back to Norwich and buried in the grounds of the Cathedral. The **Erpingham Gate** was built by Sir Thomas Erpingham who led the English archers at Agincourt in 1415 and whose statue occupies a niche over the arch. The gate leads into the tranquil Cathedral Close, where some of the houses originated as monastic buildings. Many of the buildings, including the Church of St Ethelbert, were destroyed in 1272 by rioting citizens.

Cathedral Interior

The glorious fan-vaulted roof is supported by mighty Norman pillars and three tiers of arches. The original wooden roof, destroyed by fire, was replaced in the 15th and 16th centuries with stone vaulting and embellished by **carved and painted wooden bosses** illustrating stories from the Bible. There are 1106 of these throughout the cathedral, of which 225 decorate the nave. To see them you will need binoculars, or the mirrors provided.

Beyond the organ screen, the **choir**, where choristers have sung for 900 years, has elaborate wooden carvings on the canopies and also on

F Spot the Peregrines

In 2009 a male peregrine took up residence on Norwich Cathedral spire, and was soon joined by a female. The Hawk and Owl Trust created a nesting platform on the cathedral spire and at Easter 2011 the first egg was laid. The birds have bred each year since then. You can watch the action on a live webcam on the cathedral website (see opposite), on a plasma screen in the Refectory (10am–noon and 2.45–5pm) and from a Peregrine Watchpoint with telescopes at certain times of year.

Above: the Cathedral's soaring spire.

G Plantation Garden

Adjoining the Catholic Cathedral of St John the Baptist, west of the city centre, the Plantation Garden (www.plantationgarden.co.uk; normally daily 9am–6pm) is one of Norwich's surprises: an idiosyncratic Victorian garden with a 'Gothic' fountain, medieval-style walls, woodland walkways, an Italian terrace and a rustic bridge. Run entirely by volunteers, it is a haven of peace and tranquillity, and a great spot for a picnic.

Above: the Italian terrace and flowerbeds at the Plantation Garden.

the misericords (the leaning seats to support the monks during long services) where medieval scenes, some of them humorous, depict strife, conquest of evil, sloth, greed and mortal sins. Behind the high altar the treasured fragments of the original bishop's throne, placed here by the Normans, lie below the modern wooden throne. Radiating from the ambulatory are small chapels housing medieval painted panels, the finest of which is the highly coloured and detailed **Despenser Retable** (*c.*1380) in St Luke's chapel.

The finely-preserved monastic **cloister**, the largest in England, links the

Above: the Pull's Ferry water gate on the River Wensum.

cathedral with the modern Refectory. Here the roof bosses can be seen more closely and the progression in style of the tracery is evidence of the long period of construction (1297–1430). On the site of the original monks' dining hall is a modern version of a Norman refectory.

The **Lower Close** where the monastic brew-house and bakehouse used to stand, is today the setting of some very desirable Georgian residences. From here Ferry Lane takes you down to **Pull's Ferry** ⓬, a medieval flint and stone water gate on the River Wensum. This was the route of the medieval canal dug to transport the Caen Cathedral stone on its last leg. From Pull's Ferry there are riverside walks, either north to the medieval **Cow Tower** and beyond, or south, crossing the bridge at the Compleat Angler and continuing on the path on the opposite side of the river.

SAINSBURY CENTRE FOR VISUAL ARTS

Art lovers should not leave Norwich without a visit to the **Sainsbury Centre for Visual Arts** (Earlham Road; www.scva.ac.uk; Tue–Fri 10am–6pm; free) at the University of East Anglia (UEA) on the outskirts of the city. Designed by acclaimed architect Norman Foster, it is a hangar-like building created to house Robert and Lisa Sainsbury's wonderful collection of art, featuring works by Picasso, Henry Moore and Giacometti juxtaposed with ethnographic pieces. Highlights include Moore's *Mother and Child* and an Inca llama effigy, which would probably have been buried as a human sacrifice. If you're driving, the UEA is well signposted. Alternatively, take bus number 25 or 25A from the city centre.

Eating Out

The Assembly House
Theatre Street; 01603-626 402; www.assemblyhousenorwich.co.uk; Mon–Sat 10am–7pm.
The Regency rooms in this historic house make a fine setting for breakfast (10am–noon), lunch (noon–2pm), pre-theatre dinner (5–6.45pm) or, most famously, afternoon tea (noon–5pm). Sandwiches, scones, cakes and pastries are beautifully presented. £–££

Delia's Restaurant/Yellows American Bar & Grill
Norwich City Football Club, Carrow Road; tel: 01603-218 705; www.deliascanarycatering.com; Restaurant: Fri–Sat 7pm until late; Yellows: Tue–Thu noon–9pm, Fri–Sat until 10pm.
If you're pushing the boat out try Delia's Restaurant offering three-course set meals. It's friendly, relaxing and the food is every bit as good as you would expect. For cheaper fare (snacks, steaks and 'the best ever burgers') opt for Yellows. Restaurant £££, Yellows £

Frank's Bar
19 Bedford Street; 01603-618 902; www.franksbar.co.uk; Tue–Thu 10am–midnight, Fri–Sat until 2am, Sun 10am–10.30pm.
A hip little café in the Norwich Lanes serving a great brunch and decent main meals with a Mediterranean twist. Laid-back atmosphere, with quirky vintage decor and very late opening hours for Norwich. £

Grosvenor Fish Bar
28 Lower Goat Lane; 01603-625 855; www.fshshop.com; Mon–Sat 11am–7pm.
In the Norwich Lanes, this is the city's best chippie, and it's been in the same family for over 30 years. The old undercroft downstairs has now opened up for diners to enjoy their meal (eat in or take away is the same price). Those who fancy a beer with their fish and chips can order their meal, and have it delivered to the Birdcage pub across the road. £

The Last Restaurant and Wine Bar
70–6 St George's Street; tel: 01603-626 626; www.lastwinebar.co.uk; Mon–Fri noon–2.30pm and 5pm–12.30am, Sat noon–2.30pm and 6pm–12.30am.
In a former Victorian shoe factory, this family-run place offers contemporary British cuisine and over 100 wines. The 'Last' refers to the foot-shaped form used to fashion shoes in the days when Norwich was a famous shoe-making centre. ££

Roger Hickman's Restaurant
79 Upper St Giles Street; tel: 01603-633 522; www.rogerhickmansrestaurant.com; Tue–Sat noon–2.30pm and 7–10pm.
The set menus at this award-winning restaurant feature delicacies such as foie gras mousse with grapefruit, plum and pickled mushrooms, followed by roast skate wing with charred leeks, onions, capers and burnt butter crumb – and mouthwatering desserts. £££

Tatlers
21 Tombland; tel: 01603-766 670; www.tatlersrestaurant.co.uk; Mon–Sat noon–2pm and 6–9pm.
Tatlers occupies a fine Victorian townhouse and offers traditional British and European dishes – with some culinary surprises. Seasonal and local ingredients are used where possible. ££

Tour 2

The Brecks

Discover the market towns of The Brecks, the wooded paths of Thetford Forest and the stunning ruins of Castle Acre in this one-day, 38-mile (61km) driving tour

The Brecks is a strange landscape of rolling sandy heaths and large tracts of thick forest. Once covered with heather, grasses, gorse and bracken, many acres are now planted with lofty pine trees, while remaining stretches of heathland are vital habitats for wildlife such as the rare stone curlew and woodlark. The very earliest signs of life can be seen at Grime's Graves, where Neolithic man dug over 400 mines and pits. Thetford Forest is a great spot for outdoor activities, while Thetford and Swaffham, both prosperous trading towns in medieval times, are the main market towns of the area.

Highlights

- Ancient House, Thetford
- High Lodge Thetford Forest
- Grime's Graves
- Oxburgh Hall
- Church of St Peter and St Paul, Swaffham
- Castle Acre Priory

THETFORD

In the heart of the Brecks **Thetford** ❶ was the ancient capital of East Anglia and is traditionally thought to have been the residence of Boudica, Queen of the Iceni Tribe. At the time of the Domesday Book it was the sixth largest settlement in the country and boasted its own cathedral. The ruins of the great Cluniac Priory can still be explored. The town was also

Left: exploring Thetford Forest.
Above: Thetford Priory.

birthplace of the famous revolutionary philosopher Thomas Paine. On a more frivolous note, Thetford features as Walmington-on-Sea in the hit BBC series *Dad's Army* and now has its very own Dad's Army Museum and a bronze statue of Captain Mainwaring sitting by the river.

Along the central White Hart Street you're unlikely to miss the charming timbered **Ancient House** (tel: 01842-752 599; www.museums.norfolk.gov.uk; Apr–Sept Tue–Sat 10am–5pm, Oct–Mar Tue–Sat 10am–4pm), a rare survival from the Tudor period and quite a contrast to Thetford's many newer builds. It is home to the **Museum of Thetford Life**, and includes replicas of the Thetford treasure discovered with a metal detector in 1979 (now in the British Museum), exhibits on flint-knapping and warrening, and a section on Prince Frederick Duleep Singh (1868–1926), last Maharajah of the Punjab, who bequeathed the house to the town in 1921.

Upon leaving the museum, turn right, passing the Church of St Peter,

F The Peddar's Way

Castle Acre was built at the crossing of the Nar beside the 46-mile (74km) Peddar's Way, the Roman road between central East Anglia and the Norfolk Coast, ending at Holme-next-the-Sea. Now a long-distance footpath it is well marked and easy going. Castle Acre, with its tempting cafés and pubs, along with accommodation, is a popular stop-off point. For information on the trail see www.nationaltrail.co.uk.

then immediately left for King Street and the **statue of Thomas Paine**. Retrace your footsteps, cross White Hart Street for Minstergate, then walk through the subway to reach **Thetford Priory** (Apr–Sept 8am–6pm, Oct–Mar 8am–4pm; free). After the graffiti-splattered subway these evocative ruins lift the spirit. Founded in the 12th century, the priory was home to treasured relics and became a magnet for pilgrims. Until its suppression by Henry VIII in 1546 this was the burial place of the earls and dukes of Norfolk.

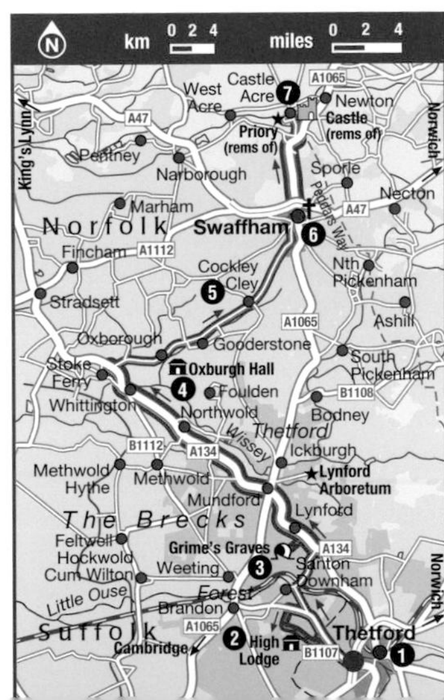

Ⓕ Thomas Paine

Thetford's most celebrated son is Thomas Paine (1737–1809), regarded as one of the greatest radical political writers of the Enlightenment. Paine emigrated to America, where he advocated American independence from Britain in his free-thinking pamphlets, but his greatest work is the *Rights of Man*, in which he espoused the cause of the French Revolution. Paine is commemorated with a statue in front of King's House, Thetford.

Above: the bronze statue of Thomas Paine in front of King's House.

THETFORD FOREST

For outdoor adventures in the forest head northwest on the B1107 for Thetford Forest. Turn left when you see signs for **High Lodge Thetford Forest** ❷ (www.forestry.gov.uk/highlodge; daily, check website for closing times; vehicle charge). To explore the forest take a walking trail or cycle path, (hire from www.bikeartthetford.co.uk), jump on board a Segway and let the kids loose at WildPlay or Go Ape (tel: 0845-643 9154; www.goape.co.uk; prebooking advisable), a great tree top adventure course with zip wires, tarzan swings and rope ladders.

GRIME'S GRAVES

Exiting the forest turn right and take the first left, a narrow road towards Santon Downham. After the village follow the road north to join the A134. Turn left and you'll soon see a sign for **Grime's Graves** ❸ (tel: 01842-810 656; www.english-heritage.org.uk; Apr–Sept daily 10am–6pm, Oct Wed–Sun 10am–5pm). This is a 96-acre (39-hectare), lunar-like landscape pitted with over 400 mine shafts. Late Neolithic miners, using antler picks and shovels made from animal shoulder blades, dug deep for the distinctive black flint, hacking through alternating layers of chalk and the paler, less desirable flint to reach the coveted third layer. One shaft is open to the public and visitors can don a hard hat and descend a 30ft (9-metre) ladder to the bottom of what was a working flint mine. The landscape here is rich in birdlife with skylarks, woodpeckers, nightjars and the very occasional stone curlew.

Rejoin the A134, and unless you want to go straight to Swaffham, cross the roundabout at Mundford, and fol-

Above: pew carving in the Church of St Peter and St Paul, Swaffham.

Above: the buttercross and statue of Ceres in Swaffham.

low the A134 for **Oxburgh Hall ❹** (www.nationaltrust.org.uk; Apr–Oct Sat–Wed and school holidays, 11am–5pm; see website for winter opening times). This is an imposing moated mansion, castle-like in its appearance, with a massive Tudor gatehouse. The mansion was built in 1482 by Sir Edmund Bedingfeld and the same family has lived here ever since. In 1950 the 9th baronet was forced to sell and the house was bought by a property developer who intended to demolish the mansion and replace it with 70 houses. But just in the nick of time three female family members sold their homes and brought the house back to the family. It has been run by the National Trust since 1952. The interior is largely Victorian and features a priest's hiding hole and needlework hangings executed by Mary Queen of Scots during her captivity.

SWAFFHAM

Continue to Swaffham via **Cockley Cley ❺**, which has a nice pub *(see p.26)* and a slightly tacky reconstructed 'Iceni Village'. At **Swaffham ❻** the main focus of life is the **Market Cross**, a large square with fine Georgian houses and a **buttercross** (where butter-sellers once displayed their wares), crowned by a statue of Ceres, Roman goddess of grain crops. The square is the scene of a weekly Saturday market and an auction selling bric-à-brac. Off Market Place the **Church of St Peter and St Paul** has a superb double hammerbeam roof, embellished with 192 carved angels. Note too the pews with medieval carvings which include a small man and a dog on a chain. This is the so-called Pedlar of Swaffham. Legend has it that a Thetford man, John Chapman, went to London to seek his fortune and met a man who dreamt he had found treasure under an oak tree in Swaffham. Chapman found the treasure and with the proceeds funded the rebuilding of the church. The Pedlar features on the town sign in Market Cross.

Last but by no means least comes **Castle Acre ❼**, marked off the main road going north from Swaffham. This is a jewel of a village, with rose-clad flint and brick cottages, heralded by the old bailey gatehouse. It is also a rare survival of a Norman planned settlement, with extensive remains of a castle, priory and massive defences. All three

G Green Britain

Just off the A47 north of Swaffham lies the Green Britain Centre (www.greenbritaincentre.co.uk; Sept–June Mon–Fri and July–Aug daily 10am–4pm; guided tours normally at 11am, 1pm and 3pm; visitor centre free, charge for turbine). The wind turbine here has a lofty viewing platform, designed by leading British architect Norman Foster. You have to climb up 300 steps for the view, but it's fairly easy going.

were built by the family of William de Warenne, a veteran of the battle of Hastings. By the late Middle Ages Castle Acre had sunk into relative obscurity, the castle was abandoned and the priory suppressed in 1537. A path off Bailey Street in the village centre leads to the west gate of the **castle** (free) on a grassy mound in glorious green countryside. The castle is thought to have been built as a combination of fortress and aristocratic residence soon after the Norman Conquest. Wander around the earthworks at this peaceful spot, then head to the far side of the village for **Castle Acre Priory** (tel: 01760-755 394; www.english-heritage.org.uk; Apr–Oct 10am–6pm, Nov–Mar 10am–5pm). One of the largest and best preserved monastic sites in the country, it is hugely atmospheric with evocative ruins in a beautiful, tranquil setting. The richly-decorated west front, intended to emphasize the prosperity and piety of its founders, is the real show-stopper but there are other substantial ruins, including the prior's lodging with rooms intact.

E Eating Out

Thetford

Elveden Estate

Brandon Road; tel: 01842-898 068; www.elveden.com; daily noon–9pm.

This award-winning pub on the Norfolk/Suffolk border is part of the Guinness-family-owned estate of Elveden, and much of the produce comes from the estate or from other local producers. The full house menu is served all day and there are various Sunday lunch options. Expect local cask ales and of course the best Guinness. £–££

Oxborough

Bedingfeld Arms

Opposite Oxburgh Hall; tel: 01366-328 300; www.bedingfeldarms.co.uk; daily noon–3pm, Tue–Sun also 6–9pm.

This late 18th-century coach house has well kept ales, spring lamb and game from the family farm, vegetables and herbs from the kitchen garden. Offerings are a notch up from the average pub: pan-seared monkfish cheeks with pea purée, rolled confit leg of lamb or pan-fried muntjac loin with broccoli and stilton purée. ££–£££

Cockley Cley

Twenty Church Wardens

Swaffham Road; tel: 01760-721 439; daily 11am–3pm, Mon–Sat also 7–11pm.

This 200-year-old ex village school serves Adnams Ales and traditional no-frills pub grub, namely home-made pies with veg and gravy (the Church Warden pie is a favourite). Full of local characters, especially on a Sunday. Cash only. £

Swaffham

The Rustic

Strattons Hotel, Ash Close; tel: 01760-723 845; www.strattons-hotel.co.uk; daily 6.30–9pm, Sun also noon–2.30pm.

This semi-basement dining restaurant in a boutique hotel regularly wins slow travel awards for its creative British cuisine. Expect welcoming staff, stylish decor and the best of regional food. The CoCoes Café and Deli offers tasty light bites and tempting cakes and pastries. ££

Castle Acre

The Ostrich

Stocks Green; tel: 01760-755 398; www.ostrichcastleacre.com; daily noon–3pm, Mon–Sat also 6–9pm.

This inviting coaching inn, which also offers accommodation, has stood on the green for over 400 years. The menu features old-fashioned favourites such as toad in the hole (with home-made sausages), bubble and squeak or beef and ale casserole. Good vegetarian dishes too. ££

Tour 3

King's Lynn to Holkham

A combination of rich heritage, seaside resorts, vast beaches and bird-rich marshes make this 40-mile (64km) tour diverse enough to suit all tastes

From historic and underrated King's Lynn this route heads north to explore the string of villages along the coast as far as Holkham. Designated as an Area of Outstanding Natural Beauty, the marshes, dunes, sand and shingle provide a haven for birdwatchers, boating enthusiasts and ramblers; while Holkham has one of the most spectacular beaches in the country. To continue from here along the coast to Cromer follow Tour 4 *(see p.36)*. If you want to leave the car at any stage the Coasthopper bus *(see p.122)* provides an excellent service from King's Lynn to Cromer, with 22 stops in between.

Highlights

- Tuesday Market Place, King's Lynn
- Sandringham Estate
- RSPB Snettisham Nature Reserve
- Houghton Hall and Gardens
- Titchwell Marsh Nature Reserve
- Holkham Hall

KING'S LYNN

On the Great Ouse, south of the Wash, **King's Lynn** ❶ was one of England's major ports from as early as the 12th century, trading with cities of northern Europe. The town was granted various royal charters, the first of them conferred by King John. Following his last visit to the city, just before he died in 1216, his royal convoy, carrying all the Crown Jewels miscalculated the tide and disappeared in the Wash. Or so the story goes. Divers have been searching for the missing treasure ever since.

The sprawling outskirts are unprepossessing but King's Lynn (or 'Lynn' as it's known) has a compact centre with many fine buildings. The town's maritime past is still very much in evidence, with restored Hanseatic warehouses, handsome former merchants' houses and a historic quay on the River Ouse.

Saturday Market Place

The huge twin-towered **King's Lynn Minster** (formerly St Margaret's Church) dominates the market place. On the other side of the square stands the magnificent **Trinity Guildhall** (now the Town Hall) with a flint and stone chequerboard facade and beside it the **Old Gaol House**, which takes you through the more gruesome aspects of the town's history. The Guildhall is about to undergo a major revamp with rooms likely to be accessible to the public by 2016.

Custom House

Take a short walk past the grand buildings and merchants' houses flanking

Preceding Page: Brancaster beach.
Above: George Vancouver statue in front of the Custom House, King's Lynn.

Queen Street. Cobbled alleys from here lead down to the river. The elegant landmark of the **Custom House** on Purfleet Quay, described by the 20th-century art historian Nikolaus Pevsner as 'one of the most perfect buildings ever' has stood here since 1683. It now serves as the tourist office and a maritime museum where

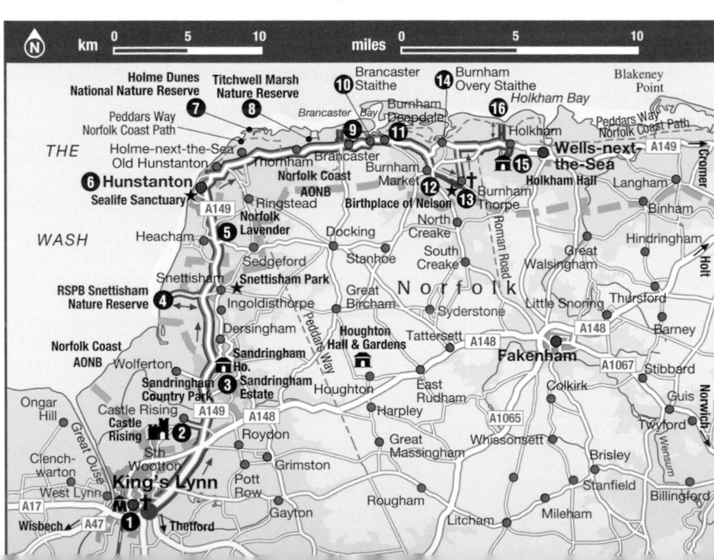

F Seahenge

In the centre of King's Lynn the Lynn Museum (Market Street; www.museums.norfolk.gov.uk; Tue–Sat 10am–5pm; free Oct–Mar) has as its centrepiece the remains of a Bronze-Age timber circle. Preserved over the centuries by peat, it was revealed in 1998 during a very low tide at Holme beach. What was assumed to be a ritualistic site was dubbed Seahenge on account of its resemblance to Stonehenge in Wiltshire. After much debate the timbers were removed to the museum for preservation.

you can find out about Lynn's famous mariners, customs men and smugglers. A statue nearby commemorates George Vancouver, a King's Lynn man who charted 5,000 miles (8,000km) of the west coast of North America in the late 18th century and gave his name to the Canadian city and island.

Tuesday Market Place

Head north along King Street, which is lined by Georgian houses. On the left is the restored early 15th-century **Guildhall of St George**, today home of the King's Lynn Arts Centre. Just beyond it the narrow Ferry Lane leads to the pedestrian ferry which crosses the Ouse to West Lynn. Occupying three acres, the grand and unspoilt **Tuesday Market Place** is one of the finest squares in the country. It is home to the **Corn Exchange** (www.kingslynncornexchange.co.uk) with a pretty neoclassical facade. This now thrives as a multi-purpose venue offering a lively programme of concerts, ballet and opera. The town's main market is held in the square on Tuesdays and Fridays.

True's Yard Fisherfolk Museum

Turn right at the end of the market, then left for **St Nicholas Chapel** (closed for renovation), founded by the Norwich bishops in 1146 and today England's largest surviving parochial chapel. Continue along St Ann's Street for **True's Yard Fisherfolk Museum** (tel: 01553-770 479; www.truesyard.co.uk; Tue–Sat 10am–4pm). Dedicated to the local fishing industry, this little museum has two restored

Below: the chequerboard facade of the Trinity Guildhall, King's Lynn.

Above: the Sandringham Estate.

fishermen's cottages, a 1904 Lynn fishing smack and the town's last remaining smokehouse. The latter was only discovered a few years ago, having been used as a tattoo parlour and fallen into disrepair. Thanks to a Heritage Lottery Fund the museum bought the premises and restored the smokehouse.

CASTLE RISING

From King's Lynn follow the A149, signposted Hunstanton. The first left turn beyond the town takes you to **Castle Rising** ❷ (Low Road; tel: 01553-631 330; www.castlerising.co.uk; Apr–Oct daily 10am–6pm, Nov–Mar Wed–Fri 10am–4pm) one of the largest and finest Norman keeps in the country. It stands at the centre of massive earthworks.

SANDRINGHAM

Follow the A149 for another 2 miles (3km) for the **Sandringham Estate** ❸ (tel: 01485-545 408; www.sandringhamestate.co.uk; daily Easter–Sept, except last week of July, house: 11am–4.45pm, Oct until 4pm; museum: 11–5pm, Oct until 4pm; gardens: 10.30am–5pm, Oct until 4pm; Country Park free). Bought in 1862 by Queen Victoria for the Prince of Wales (Edward VII to be) and his new wife, Princess Alexandra, the estate passed down through four generations of monarchs and is now the country retreat of the Queen. The house is surrounded by the 600-acre (243-hectare) **Country Park**. There is no charge to the public and

Above: relaxing at Norfolk Lavender.

many visitors come for picnics, cycle rides and nature trails through the woodland or for the shops, restaurant or café at the well-organised Visitor Centre. Visitors can also see the beautiful medieval **Church of St Mary Magdalene** where the Royal Family worship while they are at Sandringham. The main ground floor rooms of the house, used by the royal family, are open to the public, as is the museum housing royal memorabilia, and 60 acres (24 hectares) of glorious gardens.

K Snettisham Park

Close to Snettisham Church and signposted from the A149 Snettisham Park (tel: 01485-542 425; www.snettishampark.co.uk; Apr–Sept daily 10am–5pm) is a working farm where children can bottle-feed orphan lambs, feed the goats and collect eggs from the hens. Fun rides on tractors take you close up to a herd of red deer with over 50 hinds and stags. For countryside trails pick up maps from the Visitor Centre.

NORFOLK LAVENDER

The A149 continues north to **Snettisham**, home to the **RSPB Snettisham Nature Reserve** ❹ well known for the spectacular winter flights of waders and wildfowl flying in from The Wash, just before high tide. From Snettisham northwards the A149 can become traffic clogged in summer, with crowds heading for the beaches. At Heacham, **Norfolk Lavender** ❺ (tel: 01485-570 384; www.norfolk-lavender.co.uk; Apr–Oct 9am–5pm, Nov–Mar 9am–4pm; free) brings in coachloads of tourists, not just for the summer blaze of colour from the lavender, but for the large gift shop, selling all manner of lavender products, the Walsingham Farm Shop, with delicious local pies and cheeses (a good spot to pick up a picnic) and the tea room. Children's attractions are the collection of rare farm breeds, the outdoor play area and Farmer Fred's Adventure Play Barn, an indoor soft play centre.

HUNSTANTON

Two miles (3km) north of Heacham, **Hunstanton** ❻ (or 'Hunston' as the locals call it) is the only East Anglian

F Houghton Hall and Gardens

One of Britain's finest Palladian houses, Houghton Hall (www.houghtonhall.com) was built in the 1720s by Britain's first Prime Minister, Sir Robert Walpole. Restored to its former glory by the Marquess of Cholmondeley, the hall remains much as it was in Walpole's day, though the collection of Old Masters was sold to Catherine the Great and are in the Hermitage in St Petersburg, Russia. The outstanding grounds feature an award-winning 5-acre (2-hectare) walled garden and a deer park.

Above: Houghton Hall.

Above: Hunstanton beach is great for families.

resort facing west, and as such enjoys some glorious sunsets over the Wash. It was here that St Edmund, King of East Anglia, is said to have landed in AD 850, the ruins of St Edmund's Chapel marking the spot. Today it is a popular family seaside resort, with a fine, gently-sloping sandy beach, and cliffs behind which are distinctive for their coloured stripes of carrstone and red and white chalk. Quiet old Hunstanton to the north is very different from the centre, where the beach with pony rides is backed by a promenade of seaside amusements, a bingo hall and a Sealife Sanctuary (www.sealife.co.uk). The sandy beach is 2 miles (3km) long and good for exploring rock pools, collecting shells or enjoying the shallow waters of the sea (though it's a long walk to the water at low tide). Searles Sea Tours (tel: 01485-534 444; www.seatours.co.uk) organize coastal trips and one-hour seal safaris. Trips depend on the tides so it's best to ring in advance.

F Nelson's Norfolk

The great naval hero pops up every where in this part of Norfolk, and it's hardly surprising. He was born at Burnham Thorpe, learnt to sail at Burnham Overy Staithe and drank at the pub now named The Lord Nelson (or so the pub claims, *see p.35*). You'll also find Nelson memorabilia in Burnham Thorpe Church. Great Yarmouth on the east coast has the only museum dedicated to Nelson *(see Tour 6, p.51)* and the soaring Nelson Monument, in what is these days a rather grim area of the town.

HOLME DUNES AND TITCHWELL MARSH NATURE RESERVES

The A149 follows the coast eastwards through a series of small villages. **Holme-next-the-Sea** is the end (or start) of the **Peddar's Way**, crossing here with the **Norfolk Coast Path** which runs all the way from here to Cromer (46 miles/74km). The sand dunes, marshes and reed beds attract waders and migrant wildfowl, as well as nesting birds such as oystercatchers and ringed plover in spring and summer. The **Holme Dunes National**

Nature Reserve ❼ is one of a series of connecting nature reserves along this coast. But the key one is **Titchwell Marsh Nature Reserve** ❽, (tel: 01485-210 779; www.rspb.org.uk; daily dawn to dusk; free) beyond Thornwell. Dubbed 'Twitchwell', it is a mix of marsh, reedbed and beach which bring thousands of migrating birds and a wide variety of species throughout the year including marsh harriers, avocets, bearded tits and bitterns.

BRANCASTER

Next along the A149 is **Brancaster** ❾ which has a wonderfully unspoilt beach, backed by the renowned Royal West Norfolk Golf Club. The village merges into **Brancaster Staithe** ❿, popular for sailing and fishing. Brancaster is famous for mussels and you can find them for sale, along with lobster, crabs, whelks and cockles, at the Crab Hut at the Staithe or dished up at The White Horse restaurant *(see p.35)*. The favourite local watering hole is **The Jolly Sailors** pub with its own Brancaster Brewery ale, a popular spot for thirsty walkers from the Norfolk Coast path, 150yds/metres away.

Below: The Lord Nelson in Burnham Thorpe, Nelson's birthplace.

THE BURNHAM VILLAGES

Between Brancaster and Holkham there are seven Burnham villages, three of them now merging as Burnham Market. Brancaster merges into **Burnham Deepdale** ⓫ which has a church with a round Saxon tower and a Norman font with carved panels of farming scenes depicting each month of the year (press the button by the curtain to light them up). **Burnham Market** ⓬, signed off to the right just after Burnham Norton, is the showpiece village, popularly known as Chelsea-on-Sea. It has a wide green of handsome Georgian houses, lovely little shops, galleries and top-notch delis. Many of the houses here are second homes; those without their own can stay at the delightful Hoste *(see p.125)*, a hub of the village.

Take the Fakenham road from Burnham Market and the first turn left for **Burnham Thorpe** ⓭, famous as Nelson's birthplace *(see opposite)*. His house disappeared long ago but you can see a plaque where it stood, south of village. The 13th-century **All Saints' Church**, where Nelson's father was rector, is full of Nelson memorabilia, including the cross and lectern which were constructed from HMS *Victory* timbers. England's great Admiral may well have taken his first sailing lesson at **Burnham Overy Staithe** ⓮ before he went to sea at the age of 12. The village was established when the River Burn silted up and boats could no longer reach the seaport, at what is now Burnham Overy Town. It is still a sailing centre, and the harbour in the creek is the starting point for seasonal ferry trips (two hours either side of high tide) to the nature reserve of Scolt Head.

Above: horse-riding along Holkham Bay.

HOLKHAM

Last but not least on the route is **Holkham**, a remarkable combination of history, architecture, wildlife and sweeping coastal landscape. It is all part of the estate of **Holkham Hall** ⓯ (tel: 01328-713 111; www.holkham.co.uk; hall: Sun, Mon and Thu noon–4pm; museum, walled gardens, play area, café and shop: daily 10am–5pm; park daily 9am–5pm).

Set within magnificent rolling parkland, the sombre Palladian facade belies a grandiose hall and state rooms with, among others, paintings by Van Dyck, Gainsborough and Rubens. The house was built for Thomas Coke, first Earl of Leicester, in the 18th century and is occupied by his descendant, Edward Coke. The remarkable number of attractions include the Bygones Museum, the extensive grounds with 18th-century walled gardens, the deer park and lake where you can hire a canoe, kayak, rowing boat or try your hand at water zorbing. Cycles can be hired to explore the estate's extensive grounds.

Below: purple sea lavender.

Holkham Bay

Access to **Holkham Bay** ⓰ is via the salt marshes, along Lady Anne's Drive opposite Holkham Hall and on a sunny day packed with parked cars (the beach can also be reached from the next resort, Wells-next-the-Sea, *see p.36*). Follow the boardwalk through pinewoods to reach what is one of the most spectacular beaches of East Anglia: a huge swathe of sands where even in peak season you can find a peaceful stretch of sand. Low tide reveals miles of beach, and in summer a mass of purple sea lavender.

E Eating Out

Snettisham

Rose and Crown

Old Church Road; tel: 01485-543 172; www.roseandcrownsnettisham.co.uk; Mon–Fri noon–2pm and 6.30–9pm, Sat–Sun food served all day. Everything you would hope from an English village pub: an ancient rose-clad inn with low ceilings and old beams, log fires, great food and ales, and a warm welcome. Seafood and samphire come from Brancaster, asparagus and strawberries from local farmers and game 'from the gentlemen in wellies in the back bar'! ££

Ringstead

The Gin Trap

6 High Street; tel: 01485-525 264; www.thegintrap.co.uk; food served Mon–Fri noon–2pm and 6.30–9pm, Sat–Sun noon–2.30pm and 6.30–9pm. Named after the traps for catching game, rather than the alcoholic spirit, this is a cosy 17th-century coaching inn with a log fire and walled garden. The Favourites Menu features fresh beer-battered haddock fillet and chips, Gin Trap burger with Holkham estate reared beef, and fish pie. Ringstead is a picturesque village on the Peddars Way footpath. £–££

Thornham

Lifeboat Inn

Ship Lane; tel: 01485-512 236; http://lifeboatinnthornham.com; daily noon–2.30pm and 6–9.30pm. An ex-smugglers' inn in a picturesque setting overlooking the marshland coastline. It is run by renowned chef Marco Pierre White so expect high quality cuisine, but a menu that still has many pub favourites. Eat in the bar, conservatory or restaurant. ££

Brancaster Staithe

The White Horse

Main Road; tel: 01485-210 262; www.whitehorsebrancaster.co.uk; daily noon–2pm and 6.30–9pm, bar menu throughout the day. Enjoy spectacular views over the tidal marsh from the conservatory restaurant. This is definitely a place to try simply-cooked local fish and seafood. Samphire comes from the salt marsh and mussels and oysters are farmed and harvested at the bottom of the garden. ££

Burnham Market

The Hoste

The Green; tel: 01328-738 777; www.thehoste.com; daily 7.30–10.30am and noon–9.15pm. Choose from one of several stylish dining areas for top-notch modern British cuisine. The focus is on fresh local seasonal produce. The succulent oysters, from beds at Brancaster, are to die for. Follow on with sea bass caught offshore, beef from local herds or game from a local estate and, if you're feeling really decadent, end with the *dessert assiette* (to share). Fine wines and excellent service. £££

Above: alfresco dining at The Hoste in Burnham Market.

Burnham Thorpe

The Lord Nelson

Walsingham Road; tel: 01328-738 241; www.nelsonslocal.co.uk; Mon–Sat noon–2.30pm and 6–9pm. Traditional village pub and so-called 'Nelson's Local' (he was born in the village), offering well-cooked pub classics and a regularly changing specials board. Ales are served straight from the cask and there are Nelson-themed tipples such as Nelson's Blood (a blend of rum and mixed spices). Large garden with children's play area. £–££

Tour 4

Wells to Cromer

This 30-mile (48km) day tour takes in some of the very best of Norfolk: dramatic seascapes, quaint coastal villages, seal-spotting at Blakeney and delicious crabs at Cromer

This route takes you from Wells-next-the-Sea to Cromer, taking in wide stretches of beach, marsh and mud flats, and pebble shores and seaside resorts. At low tide the sea almost disappears into the distance leaving a wealth of seashells and shallow pools for children to play in. Inland the landscape is gently rolling with pretty villages, flint cottages and plenty of welcoming pubs. Be aware that the A149 is very narrow in parts and villages like Cley-next-the-Sea can become traffic-clogged in high season. The western stretch of the north Norfolk coast is covered in Tour 3 *(see p.27)*.

Highlights

- Wells-next-the-Sea
- Seal Trips from Morston
- Blakeney
- Cley Marshes Nature Reserve
- Sheringham Park
- Felbrigg Hall
- Cromer Pier

WELLS-NEXT-THE-SEA

Before the silting up of the harbour, **Wells-next-the-Sea** ❶ really did sit next to the sea. It was a major port of East Anglia and whelks were its main industry. Although a shadow of its former self, it is still a working port. Fishing boats bring in crabs, lobsters and whelks, and coasters still anchor along the quayside. The Dutch North Sea clipper, *Albatros*, dating from 1899,

Left: seal-spotting trip to Blakeney Point. **Above**: colourful beach hut, Wells-next-the-Sea.

is a permanent feature here, offering real ales and Dutch specialities above and below deck, live music at weekends and even bed and breakfast. The resort has a lively centre with small shops, abundant cafés, chippies and stalls selling seafood. It also has a lovely leafy Georgian square, called the Buttlands, with two former coaching inns both offering attractive accommodation and fine dining.

Retail Treats

Cley-next-the-Sea's High Street boasts a fine selection of little shops: the family-run Cley Smokehouse (www.cleysmokehouse.com) where everything is smoked on site, the neighbouring Made In Cley (www.madeincley.co.uk) with tempting pieces of pottery made on the premises, the Pink Foot Gallery (www.pinkfootgallery.co.uk) devoted to contemporary nature-inspired art and Picnic Fayre (www.picnic-fayre.co.uk), an award-winning deli in an historic old forge. Inland, Holt has some fine art galleries, two excellent bookshops, several stylish clothes boutiques, plus Bakers and Larners (www.bakersandlarners.co.uk), described by some as 'the Fortnum & Mason of East Anglia'.

The Beach

The vast and dramatic sandy beach, backed by pine-clad dunes, is a mile from the centre, and can be accessed either by foot along **The Bank** or on the narrow-gauge harbour railway. At low tide it's over a mile down to the water's edge, but when the tide turns it comes in fast and can catch tourists

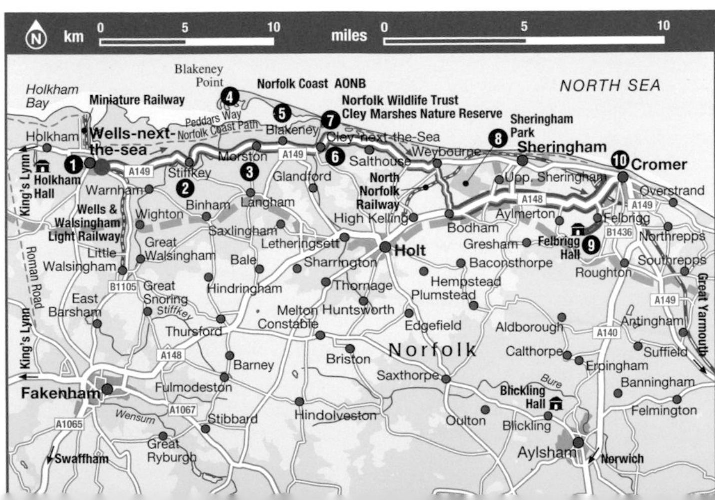

Above: paddling at Blakeney Point.

unaware. This is probably Norfolk's best surveyed beach, equipped with a volunteer coast watch, official life-guards and a World War II siren which blares out when the tide turns and can be heard from a distance of five miles (8km).

STIFFKEY

The A149 passes right through the little village of **Stiffkey** ❷, traditionally famous for 'Stewkey blues', or cockles, collected from the salt marshes to the north of the village and coloured blue from the mud. Today, however, any cockles you find on menus or at seafood stalls will have come from King's Lynn. The **Rescue Wooden Boats** Charitable Trust (www.rescuewoodenboats.com) are working to restore and re-use crab and whelk boats and other heritage working craft. Their Visitor Centre (Sat–Sun 10am–4pm) is signed to the left off the main road.

BLAKENEY

Next along is **Morston** ❸, where ferries depart from the quay for seal-spotting trips to **Blakeney Point** ❹ (tel: 0800-074 0753; www.bishopsboats.com; Mar–Oct daily according to tides; advance booking advisable). Blakeney Point is home to a colony of common and grey seals, which bask on the sands when the tide is low. Trips last roughly an hour but when tides and conditions allow, boats can also stop on Blakeney Point Nature Reserve, adding between 30 minutes and 1 hour to the trip. The tip of Blakeney Point is the summer home of about a dozen species of seabirds, including a large colony of terns.

Blakeney ❺ itself, a little further on, is a lovely little coastal village of flint-cobbled cottages, with a fine church and a tiny harbour with small yachts and footpaths along mudflats and salt marshes. Birdwatchers flock here all year round and it's very popular for sailing. Like so many of the coastal villages, Blakeney was a major harbour before the silting up of the estuary. Now only small boats can navigate the waters.

CLEY-NEXT-THE-SEA

East of Blakeney, **Cley-next-the Sea** ❻ (pronounced 'Cly') became

F The North Norfolk Steam Railway

The resort of Sheringham was a small fishing village before the North Norfolk Railway was established in 1887. It was axed 77 years later by Dr Beeching, but local enthusiasts were determined to preserve Norfolk's most scenic stretch of railway, with steam services starting in 1976. The scenic Poppy Line of The North Norfolk Steam Railway (www.nnrailway.co.uk), operated largely by volunteers, carries over 150,000 passengers a year and chugs five miles (8km) between Sheringham and the lovely little Georgian town of Holt.

Above: conducter on The North Norfolk Steam Railway.

the first Wildlife Trust nature reserve in 1926. The combination of salt marshes, reed beds and lagoons attract a remarkable amount of birdlife, both breeding and migratory. Details of local sitings are on display at the excellent eco-friendly Visitor Centre (daily 10am–5pm, until 4pm in winter; free) of the **Norfolk Wildlife Trust Cley Marshes Nature Reserve** ❼ beyond the village on the right. Lazy birders can sit in the panoramic café with its wonderful coastal views, spotting birds using the telescopes provided. Serious ones will spend the day in the reeds and marshes, or in the hides that provide fine views over saline pools and scrapes. There is good birding all year round, whether it's spotted redshank in spring, avocet or spoonbills in summer, waders in August and September or wildfowl in winter. Birds apart, Cley is a delightful village of flint and brick cottages and enticing little shops *(see p.37)*. A prominent landmark is the 18th-century **Cley Windmill**, which has been converted into a very appealing guesthouse *(see p.125)*. The architectural highlight of the village is the **Church of St Margaret** on the Holt Road, a glorious medieval church, with a soaring tower, beautifully carved porch and fine carvings inside. Sadly the work on the church in the 14th century was never completed. The Black Death in 1349 killed half the population of Cley and work came to a standstill.

Below: Cley Windmill.

SHERINGHAM PARK

Continue along the A149 through Salthouse to Weybourne, turning

Above: the walled garden at Felbrigg Hall.

right opposite the church, then immediately left, following signs to Bodham. When you reach the A148 turn left. In about 1½ miles (2km) you will see a sign for **Sheringham Park** ❽ (tel: 01263-820 550; www.nationaltrust.org.uk; daily dawn to dusk; free but charge for parking) designed in 1812 by the landscape gardener, Humphry Repton. This splendid 1,000-acre (405-hectare) park has landscaped and woodland gardens with some stunning coastal views, particularly from the Gazebo, a tower at treetop height. The park can be explored on waymarked trails.

FELBRIGG HALL

Continue on the A148 for about 4 miles (6km), turning right on to the B1436, signed **Felbrigg Hall** ❾ (tel: 01263-837 444; www.nationaltrust.org.uk; early Mar–Oct daily 11am–5pm), a wonderful Jacobean mansion filled with 18th-century furnishings and paintings collected on the Grand Tour. No less impressive is the extensive parkland with woodland and lakeside paths and a lovely walled garden with espalier fruit trees, abundant flowering plants and an 18th-century octagonal dovecote.

CROMER

The final stop is **Cromer** ❿, dramatically poised on a high bluff. This pleasantly old-fashioned seaside resort became popular with the advent of the railway. Behind the long sand and shingle beach the town centre is dominated by its parish church whose soaring tower, with 172 steps, is the tallest in Norfolk. Cromer is best known for its pier, whose Pavilion Theatre still packs in audiences, and for the famous Cromer crab, sold

Below: Cromer Pier.

throughout Norfolk from Easter to October. You won't have to go far in town before finding a stall or restaurant offering Cromer dressed crab.

Cromer Pier

The splendid Cromer Pier lies below the Victorian Hôtel de Paris, whose guest list includes the Prince of Wales (the future Edward VII) and Oscar Wilde who stayed here in 1892. One of the few surviving piers along the East Anglian coastline, it has a café, gift shop, a life boat station and the only 'End of the Pier Show' in Europe. Cromer's **Pavilion Theatre** (www.cromer-pier.com) has been producing a live variety show for the past 37 years. Shows take place from Easter to September and are full of glitz and glamour, with West End and Broadway style song and dance numbers. Celebrities appear from time to time.

A tidal surge in December 2013 nearly put a stop to the show. This wouldn't have been the first disaster. The wooden jetty built in 1822 was swept away in a storm, the replacement washed away before the paint was barely dry, the third lasted until

Above: seafront supper, Cromer.

1897 when it was torpedoed amidships by a coal boat during a storm. Today's pleasure pier dates from 1901. Despite an attempt to blow it up in World War II to prevent it being used as a landing stage by invading forces, damage wrought by the 1953 and 2013 tidal surges and a bulk barge slicing through it in 1993, it is still here today – a testament to Victorian engineering.

Cromer Museums and Zoo

At the end of the promenade the **Henry Blogg Museum** (tel: 01263-511 294; www.rnli.org.uk/henryblogg; Apr–Sept Tue–Sun 10am–5pm, Oct–

F Blickling Hall

Ten miles (16km) south of Cromer, Blickling Hall (www.nationaltrust.org.uk; Wed–Mon 10.15am–5.30pm; weekends only in winter; park free) creates quite an impact: a magnificent red-brick Jacobean mansion crowned by turrets, chimneys and gables. The interior gives you an insight into both upstairs and downstairs life in the Edwardian era but the extensive grounds are the main attraction with a lake amidst the park and woodland. There are several miles of footpaths and bridle paths and cycles can be hired.

Above: exploring the gardens at Blickling Hall.

Mar until 4pm; free) is named after Cromer's celebrated coxwain (1876–1954) who served for 53 years, saved 873 lives and became a national hero. The centrepiece is Blogg's life boat, *H.F. Bailey*. Inland, next to Cromer Church, the **Cromer Museum** (tel: 01263-513 543; www.museums.norfolk.gov.uk; Mon–Fri 10am–4pm, Sat noon–4pm, Apr–Oct also Sun 1–4pm) gives you an insight into Cromer when it was a Victorian seaside resort with fine hotels. South of the town the **Amazona Zoo** (Hall Road; tel: 01263-510 741; www.amazonazoo.co.uk; Apr–Nov daily 10am–5pm) has animal species from tropical South America in a wooded setting. The zoo works with conservationists and the animals are not taken from the wild.

E Eating Out

Wells-next-the-Sea

The Crown Hotel

The Buttlands; tel: 01328-710 209; www.crownhotelnorfolk.co.uk; daily noon–2.30pm and 6.30–9pm.
Part of The Flying Kiwi Inns group, owned by New Zealand-born celebrity chef Chris Coubrough, this boutique hotel offers fine dining in the restaurant's spacious orangery. Afternoon teas are on offer too – with or without Prosecco. ££–£££

Blakeney

Blakeney Hotel

The Quay; tel: 01263-740 797; www.blakeney-hotel.co.uk; daily noon–2pm and 6.30–9pm, Sat until 9.30pm.
One of the coast's loveliest hotels, the Blakeney serves first-class food with fine views across the estuary. Non-residents are welcome at breakfast, lunch or dinner. Come for Blakeney fish soup, home-made burgers, whole dressed local crab, fillet of sea bass or roast Norfolk fillet of beef. ££–£££

Morston

Morston Hall

A149 between Blakeney and Stiffkey; tel: 01263-741 041; www.morstonhall.com; dinner daily at 7.30pm, lunch Sun at 12.30pm.
Luxury dining in a smart country house hotel. Michelin-starred chef Galton Blackiston features local produce such as Blakeney lobster and Morston mussels on the menu. The dinner tasting menu of six courses changes daily. Reservations essential. £££

Cromer

Mary Jane's Fish Bar

27–9 Garden Street; tel: 01263-511 208; daily 11.30am–11pm.
A favourite Cromer chippie, which usually has long queues outside. You can eat the fish and chips in the basic restaurant, or enjoy them on the nearby cliffs or beach. £

No 1 Cromer

1 New Street; tel: 01263-512 316; www.no1cromer.com; downstairs: daily noon–3pm and 4.30–8.30pm; upstairs: Wed–Sun noon–3pm and 5.30–9pm; Ice Cromer 11am–8pm.
Upmarket chippie opened by Galton Blackiston of Morston Hall *(see left)* and an upstairs restaurant with great sea, pier and sunset views. The short menu features Cromer crab burger, sharing tapas, cockled popcorn and Japanese pork belly sliders. End with a hot sugar donut or ice cream at Ice Cromer on the corner of New Street. ££

Holt

Byfords

1–3 Shirehall Plain; tel: 01263-711 400; www.byfords.org.uk; daily 8am–9.30pm.
This 'posh B&B' with its own delicatessen is open all day for breakfast, morning coffee and home-made cakes, light lunches, clotted-cream teas or candlelit dinners. Choose from soups, salads and pasties, grazing dishes to share, pizzas or pasta, house curry, local beef or Byford's kedgeree. £

Tour 5

Norfolk Broads

This whole day 34-mile (55km) driving tour, with optional walks and boat trips, explores the timeless landscape of the Norfolk Broads, the largest protected wetland in the UK

Norfolk's main tourist draw, the Broads are an extensive network of navigable rivers and lakes, fens, marshes and wet woodlands. The shallow lakes, or broads, were created by the gradual flooding of shallow pits which had been created by medieval peat-diggers. Today the waterways are a haven for boating holidaymakers, walkers, cyclists and wildlife enthusiasts. Although much of the plant and animal life has disappeared, many of the broads are now nature reserves. Remember to wear sturdy shoes or wellies – this is a wetland, even in summer. If time allows, take one of the small boat trips from various spots across the Broads – there's nothing like seeing them from the water.

Highlights

- Ranworth Broad Wildlife Centre
- Church of St Helen, Ranham
- BeWILDerwood
- Hickling Broad
- Horsey Windpump and Seals at Horsey

RANWORTH BROAD

Start your tour 4 miles (6km) east of Wroxham at the village of **Ranworth**, peacefully set on the Malthouse Broad in the valley of the River Thurne. Norfolk Wildlife Trust runs boat trips from here to the superb floating **Ranworth Broad Wildlife Centre** ❶ (free) where visitors can take another boat for a tour around the broad. Alternatively take the 10–15 minute walk along the leafy boardwalk via reed and sedge beds with rare aquatic plants. Look out for rare butterflies, dragonflies and damsel flies as you go. The glass-panelled wildlife centre has wonderful views of wildfowl on the water. This is a family-friendly spot with chatty staff and plenty of nature activities for children. Carefully positioned webcams focus on the antics of the wildfowl on the water. There are always birds to see, especially terns diving for fish.

Back at Ranworth don't miss the **Church of St Helen** ❷ above the village. Known as 'the Cathedral of the Broads', this has a beautifully decorated medieval roodscreen portraying the apostles and popular saints of the period, a rare illuminated anti phoner (service book) and – for the energetic – glorious views from the top of the bell tower (89 steep steps up).

Preceding Page: canoeing on Wroxham Broad. **Above**: the view from the Church of St Helen, Ranworth.

SALHOUSE BROAD AND HOVETON GREAT BROAD

Drive from Ranworth to Salhouse via the pretty village of **Woodbastwick** ❸ with its thatched houses. Before the village of Salhouse you'll see a wooden sign for **Salhouse Broad** ❹ (tel: 01603-722 775; www.salhousebroad.org.uk), a broad of around 40 acres (16 hectares) reached by a 10-minute woodland walk. This is a popular spot for canoe hire, as well as ferry trips (crossings Thu and Sun 10am–4pm) to the nature trail on **Hoveton Great Broad** ❺, another haven for wildlife.

WROXHAM

Drive on to Salhouse, turning right for **Wroxham** ❻. Be forewarned that this small town's centre is notorious for

Wroxham Barns

North of Wroxham on the Tunstead Road the Wroxham Barns complex (www.wroxhambarns.co.uk; daily 10am–5pm) is a favourite with youngsters, particularly for its Junior Farm where children can watch pigs being fed, groom the ponies, collect eggs from the henhouse and bottle-feed spring lambs. The site includes craft studios, clothes boutiques, a play area and a mini-golf course. There is also an excellent restaurant *(see p.49)*.

Above: children will love the Junior Farm at Wroxham Barns.

traffic jams, especially at weekends. The so-called Capital of the Norfolk Broads, it is a boaties' paradise, equipped with every nautical need. The famous Roys of Wroxham, in the same family since the 19th century, appear to own half the village, and have what's universally known as 'the world's biggest village store'. Stock up in their Food Hall for a picnic or head straight on taking the main right turn after the bridge sign-posted Potter Heigham, A1062.

BEWILDERWOOD

Just before Horning you'll see signs for **BeWILDerwood** ❼ (tel: 01692-633 033; www.bewilderwood.co.uk; February half term until end of October half term, 10am–5.30pm, but check website before visiting). If you have children in tow, particularly 2–12-year-olds, this is not to be missed. There's oodles of fun here. Extending over 50

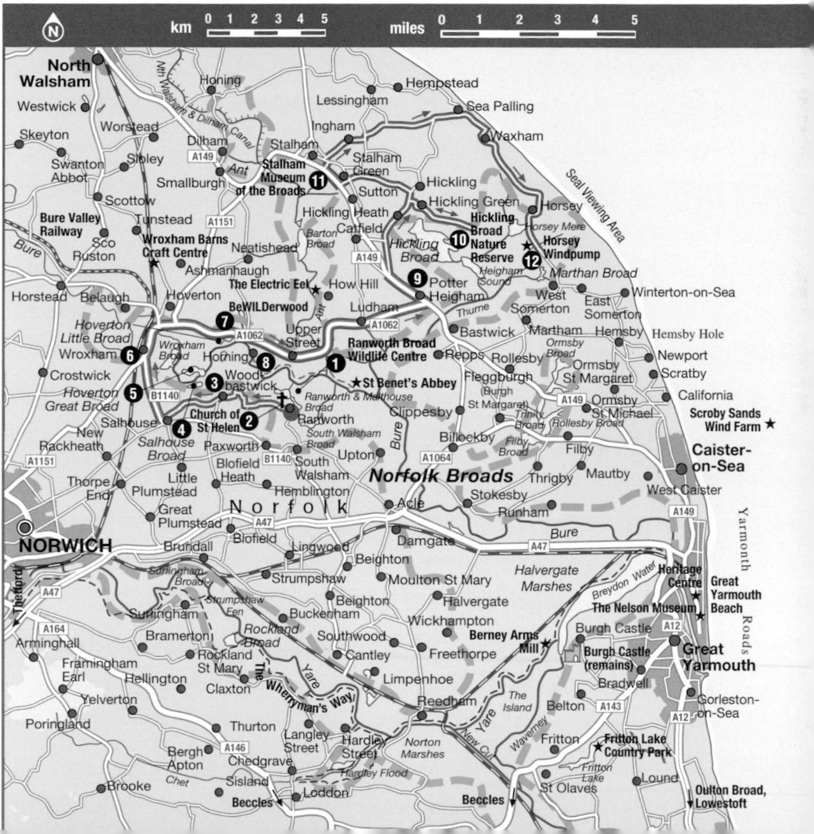

Spot the Seals

Horsey is only about a mile from the sea and the beach between here and Winterton-on-Sea is home to a colony of seals that come to breed. Turn left before you reach the Windpump, along a track marked 'seal viewing area'. From here it's a 20-minute walk – and well worth it as you can often see seals bobbing up and down in the waves. In winter you can see large numbers of them offshore.

Above: a couple of friendly seals near Horsey.

acres of woodland and marshland, it is a magical playground of tree-houses, aerial ropewalks and wobbly zip-wires, reached by boat or boardwalk. The whole site is built from sustainable wood. Creator and owner Tom Blofeld drew on happy childhood memories (he grew up here) to create the adventure playground and the magical forest folk who live deep in the woods, among them Swampy, a young Marsh Boggle, the lugubrious Thornyclod Spider and the goblin-like Twiggles. The characters feature in Tom's wonderful book *A Boggle at BeWILDerwood* which, with his other books (and audio book), are on sale at the site.

HORNING

Take the next right turn for the pretty riverside village of **Horning** ❽. If you're in need of sustenance there is plenty of choice here: the Swan Inn has a lovely setting by the waterside and the Horning Fish Bar has won the Best Broadland Chippie award several years running. A plaque in the centre of Horning shows the path from the village along the River Bure to **St Benet's Abbey**. The evocative 12th-century ruin, standing in isolation, was originally on an island and has become an iconic symbol of the Broads. This is still a place of worship and the Bishop of Norwich takes an annual service here on the first Sunday of August. A conservation project is underway.

HICKLING BROAD

Continue east along the A1062 through the quiet village of Ludham for **Potter Heigham** ❾, a boating centre best known for its low-arched medieval bridge where many an amateur sailor has floundered. There is

Above: treehouses at BeWILDerwood.

Above: pleasure boating on Horning Broads.

little to detain you in the village so turn left on to the A149, signed Stalham. Take the first right turn, marked Hickling, and follow signs to the village which bring you to the Greyhound Inn, an excellent place for a pit stop, *see p.49*). Turn right at the pub, following signs for the Nature Reserve and Visitor Centre.

Set in the upper stretches of the River Thurne **Hickling Broad** (www.norfolkwildlifetrust.org.uk/hickling) is the largest of the Norfolk Broads. With its wide skies and open landscape it's a lovely spot for a walk. Various trails start from the **Nature Reserve** ⑩. Keep an eye out for swallowtail butterflies, bitterns, cranes, lapwings, marsh harriers and other birds and insects. The Water Trail takes you by electric-powered boat across open water to the 60ft (18-metre) tree tower with its views of the Broad. It's worth hiring binoculars from the Visitor Centre (deposit required), and booking is recommended for boat trips (tel: 01603-625 540).

STALHAM MUSEUM OF THE BROADS

Return to the Greyhound Inn, turn right and take the second left towards Stalham. After just over 2 miles (3km) turn left and immediately right for the A149, then head towards Stalham. You'll see the **Stalham Museum of the Broads** ⑪ (The Staithe; tel: 01692 581 681; www.museumofthebroads.org.uk; early Apr–Oct daily 10.30am–5pm) signed on the left before you reach the village. Manned by dedicated volunteers, this is a small but informative set-up where you can discover how the landscape was forged, learn about wherries which traded here, watch footage of early Broads' holiday life and see a fine collection of Broads' boats.

F Bure Valley Railway

Let the train take the strain and enjoy the views of Bure Valley from the narrow gauge railway which runs between Wroxham and the market town of Aylsham. This old-fashioned railway operates from April to October (www.bvrw.co.uk) with a journey time of 45 minutes. The train stops at Coltishall, Buxton and Brampton en route. You can also walk or pedal along the Valley Path that follows the railway.

Above: train and driver on the Bure Valley Railway.

Above: sailboat on Oulton Broad.

HORSEY WINDPUMP

Turn left on to the A149 and first right, following brown signs all the way to **Horsey Windpump** ⓬ (tel: 01493-393 450; www.nationaltrust.org.uk; check website for opening times). The pump dates from 1912 and was restored in 1943 by the National Trust after damage by lightning. Climb to the top to enjoy fine views over the pretty **Horsey Mere**. After a bracing walk along the beach to see the seals *(see p.46)* the cosy Nelson Head pub in **Horsey** *(see p.49)* makes a welcome retreat.

SOUTHERN BROADS

In comparison to their northern neighbours the Southern Broads are less scenic, with fewer facilities but also less crowded. The main road access is via Lowestoft, Norwich or **Loddon**, a lively little market town and boating centre on the River Chet. Many of the broads are inaccessible by car and you're better off going by boat, foot – or even train. **The Wherryman's Way** is the main long-distance footpath of the Broads (35 miles/56km) following the River Yare from Great Yarmouth all the way to Norwich. From Great Yarmouth the path leads to the huge expanse of **Breydon Water**, a tidal estuary rather than a Broad, revealing a vast expanse of mud at low tide. This gateway from the sea to the Broads is a haven for geese, ducks and waders – the RSPB have a nature reserve here with a bird hide.

Fine views over Breydon Water and Halvergate grazing marshes can be seen from the Roman fort remains of **Burgh Castle** *(see Tour 6, p.53)*. The Wherryman's Way continues to **Berney Arms** with a lofty windmill, wonderful views of the marshes and a remote, cosy pub. There is no road access but it has its own railway station. The path continues to **Reedham**, a busy spot renowned for its swing railway bridge and chain ferry for cars. This is the only place where you can cross the Yare between Great Yarmouth and Norwich so expect queues in summer. Further along the river is the minor but beautiful **Rockland Broad** and to the northwest **Surlingham**, popular for its pubs and walks in the Wheatfen Nature Reserve. The most southerly Broad, and the one most easily accessible by car is **Oulton Broad** *(see Tour 6, p.54)* near Lowestoft.

Ⓕ The *Electric Eel*

Explore a working marsh on the *Electric Eel* (Apr, May and Oct Sat–Sun, bank holidays, Easter week and half terms) departing from Toad Hole Cottage, How Hill, northeast of Horning. The electrically-powered Edwardian-style boat glides through the dykes where reed and sedge are cut annually for thatch. Toad Hole Cottage, formerly an eel-catcher's cottage, is now an information point and study centre for the Broads.

E Eating Out

Woodbastwick

The Fur and Feather Inn

Slad Lane; tel: 01603-720 003; www.thefurandfeatherinn.co.uk; food: Mon–Sat 10am–9pm, Sun 10am–8pm; bar: Mon–Thu 10am–8pm, Fri–Sat until 11pm, Sun 10am–9.30pm.

The tap for the neighbouring Woodforde's Brewery, this is an alluring thatched pub with top notch ales and home-made food. Along with pub classics there are puff pastry pies, such as venison and merlot or pheasant and bacon. Beer fans can finish off with chocolate ale cake flavoured with malted cream and Norfolk Nog shooter. Bottled beers, gifts and locally-sourced produce can be purchased from the adjacent brewery. ££

Wroxham

Wroxham Barns

Tunstead Road; tel: 01603-777 106; www.wroxhambarns.co.uk; daily 10am–5pm.

Just north of Wroxham (and part of the Wroxham Barns complex, *see p.44*) this welcoming, award-winning restaurant serves excellent home-made snacks and lunches. Try the chowder with locally-smoked haddock, the delicious rarebit or the lamb or pork from the local Swannington Farm. And leave room for the Norfolk treacle tart. £–££.

Horstead

The Recruiting Sergeant

Norwich Road; tel: 01603-737 077; www.recruitingsergeant.co.uk; Mon–Fri noon–2pm and 6.30–9pm, Sat–Sun noon–9pm.

In the village of Horstead, near Coltishall, this gastropub is a great place for locally caught fish and seafood, Norfolk beef and pork and Sunday roasts. The menu is more sophisticated than the average Norfolk pub, but you can just opt for fish and chips. ££

Hickling

The Greyhound Inn

The Green; tel: 01692-598 306; www.greyhoundinn.com; daily noon–8.30pm.

An alluring country pub with a good choice of well-kept local and guest real ales. Meat and seasonal produce is locally sourced wherever possible – Cromer crabs are a favourite in summer. Meals can be taken on the sunny front terrace, in the cottage garden, by a roaring fire or in the more formal dining room. ££

Horsey

Nelson Head

The Street; tel: 01493-393 378; Mon–Sat 11am–3pm and 6–11pm, until 10pm Mon–Wed in winter, Sun noon–3pm and 6–10pm.

This is a real traditional Norfolk pub, where walkers, boaters and locals are welcomed with local Woodforde's ales, home-made meals, a roaring fire in winter and a large garden for summer. Unsurprisingly Nelson memorabilia forms part of the decor. ££

Above: lunchtime drinks by St Olaves Broad.

Stokesby

The Ferry Inn

The Green; tel: 01493-751 096; www.ferryinn.net; food: Mon–Fri noon–2pm and 6–9pm, Sat–Sun noon–9pm.

The idyllic setting on the River Bure and the cosy friendly interior make this a firm favourite with both locals and tourists. Visitors on boats can moor up here free of charge and if there's no room at the inn dishes can be taken out and enjoyed on board. Helpings are generous, prices are fair. £–££

Tour 6

Great Yarmouth

This 30-mile (48km) day tour of contrasts takes in the spirited coastal resorts of Great Yarmouth and Lowestoft, and peaceful cultural highlights inland

Great Yarmouth used to be one of the wealthiest cities in the country. Before World War I over a thousand fishing trawlers were engaged in the industry, but over-fishing and competition from abroad led to a steep decline and the town today relies on servicing container ships, North Sea oil rigs and renewable energy sources. Yarmouth (as it used to be known) has been a seaside resort since 1760 and today boasts splendid sands and non-stop entertainment. It is a town of two very different parts: the holiday resort focussed on the marina, where golden sands are hidden from view behind the roller coasters, and the historic quarter of South Quay. Parking here can be tricky so leave the car along the seafront and walk across to the quayside.

Highlights

- Heritage Quarter and beach, Great Yarmouth
- Somerleyton Hall and Gardens
- Maritime Museum and South Beach, Lowestoft
- Oulton Broad

HERITAGE QUARTER

The town's **Heritage Quarter** ❶ stretches along South Quay. Almost opposite the Town Hall the ***Lydia Eva*** (www.lydiaeva.org.uk; Apr–Oct, daily 10am–4pm; free) is the last surviving steam drifter of the herring fleet based in Great Yarmouth. A boat hand will show you round and talk nostalgically of the herring fleet in its

Left: the Pleasure Beach, Great Yarmouth. **Above**: the Nelson Museum.

heyday when a drifter like the *Lydia Eva* would cast 65 nets out to sea. Cross the road for the **Elizabeth House Museum** (tel: 01493-855 746; www.nationaltrust.org.uk; Apr–Oct Sun–Fri 10am–4pm), a much restored Tudor house built by a wealthy merchant and laid out to give you an idea of domestic life in the 16th century. Legend has it that a meeting to decide the fate of Charles I (death by execution) was held in the grander of the rooms, known as 'the Conspiracy Room'. Cromwell is said to have visited the house on several occasions.

Continue along South Quay for the **Nelson Museum** (tel: 01493-850 698; www.nelson-museum.co.uk; Feb–Nov Mon–Fri 10am–4pm, Sat–Sun 1–4pm), which tells the story of the national hero, covering his complex love life and affair with Emma Hamilton as well as his naval career. Children can dress up in period costume and walk the wobbly plank.

Behind the Nelson Museum a series of narrow alleys, known as **The Rows**, originally separated medieval tenements. The alleys housed wealthy merchants at one end and bars and brothels at the other. Many of the Row houses were destroyed in World War II or demolished after the war, but the **Old Merchant's House** and **Row III** have been preserved. The nearby **Toll House**, once a medieval gaol, dwells on the fate of criminals and the tales of gaolers.

If you happen to be here during the week, don't miss the **Smoke-**

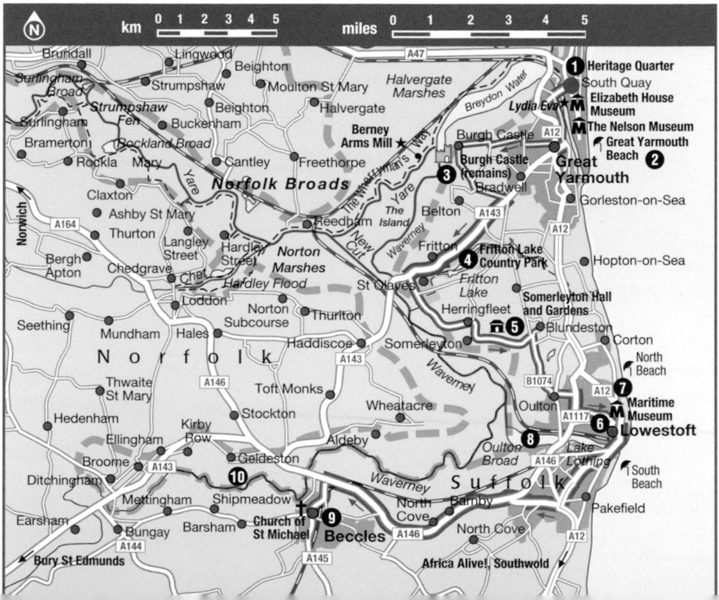

K African Animals

At Kessingland, south of Lowestoft, Africa Alive! (tel: 01502-740 291; www.africa-alive.co.uk; daily from 9.30am) presents the sights and sounds of Africa. Feed a meerkat, meet the aardvarks, and see giraffes, zebras, lions, rhino and many more species. There is ample to keep youngsters entertained including feeding talks, a farmyard corner, a discovery centre and an adventure play area. Africa Alive! supports conservation projects in the wild to help secure the future of endangered species.

house Museum and Pottery (tel: 01493-850 585; www.greatyarmouth potteries.co.uk; late Apr–Oct Mon–Fri 9.30am–3pm, July–Sept until 4pm) due south of the Toll House in a former herring smokehouse. This fascinating historic building, with a medieval wall, is constructed from driftwood, tarred timbers and pieces from old shipwrecks. It is a fully working pottery, with information on the herring

Below: Great Yarmouth rock for sale.

smoking industry and a gallery packed with nautical memorabilia.

The nearby **Time and Tide Museum** (tel: 01493-743 930; www.museums.norfolk.gov.uk; early Apr–Oct daily 9.30am–4.30pm, Nov–Mar Mon–Fri 10am–4pm, Sat–Sun noon–4pm) covers the rise and decline of the fishing industry. The museum occupies the site of a Victorian herring curing works, where the aroma of smoked fish still lingers. Homes of local fishermen and a 1950s fish wharf are recreated and visitors can take the wheel of a coastal drifter. In the Seaside Gallery a collection of postcards and posters, souvenirs and a 'What the Butler Saw' Mutoscope celebrate Great Yarmouth's heyday as a booming seaside resort. There are plenty of hands-on activities to keep children amused.

Marine Parade

Be prepared for a neon-lit stretch of amusement arcades and a long row of garish attractions along the golden sands of **Great Yarmouth Beach ❷**. If you have children in tow there are non-stop activities: rides and chutes on the beach; horse-drawn carriages; miniature train rides; the Merrivale Model Village; the Sea Life aquarium; and Amazonia, offering close encounters with snakes, alligators and even baby crocs. And if that's not enough there is always Pleasure Beach further south, with fairground rides galore. Alternatively just buy a bucket and spade for a good time on the golden sands.

THE ROYAL HOTEL

A few buildings along the front hint at Great Yarmouth's heyday. Opposite the Sealife aquarium, the Royal Hotel dates back to the 18th century. It used to be called the Post House as this was the pick-up point for the Royal Mail and also for passengers of the London Stage Coach. Dickens stayed here in 1848

Above: a potter at work at the Smokehouse Museum and Pottery.

and you can see a signed copy of his dinner menu hanging up in reception. Another famous guest was Edward VII, eldest son of Queen Victoria, who (according to the hotel) entertained his famous mistress here, the actress Lillie Langtry. Lillie made regular appearances on stage at the Royal Aquarium.

BURGH CASTLE

From Great Yarmouth take the Beccles Road, turning right at the roundabout before the road joins the A12. From here brown signs will direct you to **Burgh Castle** ❸ (tel: 0870-222 1181; www.english-heritage.org.uk; free). The impressive remains of the fort lie about 20 minutes' walk from the car park. This was one of nine forts on the Saxon Shore, built in AD 300 but probably abandoned 100 years later. The sheer size of the surviving walls is remarkable and the site, overlooking Breydon water and surrounding marshes, is spectacular.

F Dickens' Yarmouth

In 1848 Charles Dickens stayed at the Royal Hotel in Great Yarmouth with his colleague and friend, Mark Lemon, and was clearly impressed with the town as he used it as a main setting for *David Copperfield.* Peggotty, the Copperfields' faithful housekeeper, tells David it was a well known fact that 'Yarmouth was, upon the whole, the finest place in the universe'.

SOMERLEYTON ESTATE

Take the A143 going south, passing **Fritton Lake Country Park** ❹ (tel: 0333-456 0777; www.fritton lake.info) on your left. This activity park, offering boating, tree-climbing, golf and walks in a lovely setting, is part of the Somerleyton Estate. To reach **Somerleyton Hall and Gardens** ❺ (tel: 0871-222 4244; www.somerleyton.co.uk; Apr–Sept Tue, Thu and Sun 10am–5pm, mid-July to mid-Sept also Wed), take the next turning left. A Victorian entrepreneur, Samuel Morton Peto, rebuilt this vast mansion in Tudor-Jacobean style. Peto went bankrupt and the house was sold to Sir Francis Crossley, whose family still own it. The interior features a splendid ballroom with white marble and crimson damask, but for many the highlight is the garden, incorporating a yew maze and a walled garden with glasshouses designed by Joseph Paxton (architect of London's Crystal Palace). From Somerleyton rejoin the B1074 going east for Lowestoft (6 miles/10km).

LOWESTOFT

England's most easterly town has seen better days. Once a thriving fishing port, **Lowestoft** ❻ now has no fishing fleet and the centre looks unloved. The plus points are its golden **South Beach** and **Oulton Broad**. The glass East Point Pavilion is a central hub, with a well-equipped tourist office. On Heritage Quay in the harbour the ***Mincarlo*** (tel: 07927-602

Above: the gardens at Somerleyton Hall.

953; www.lydiaeva.org.uk; normally June–Oct 10am–4pm but check website for details; voluntary donation) is one of the few reminders of Lowestoft's heyday: the last of its sidewinder trawlers.

Lowestoft was built on the clifftops and in the early 19th century was famous for its 'hanging gardens' which cascaded from merchants' houses to the base of the cliffs. The merchants had fishing or shipbuilding businesses and used ancient thoroughfares known as scores, named after local characters or public inns, to get down to the north beach area. Some of the scores can still be seen today, while the best examples of Lowestoft's oldest houses, which survived World War II, can be seen along the High Street.

G Scroby Sands

Scroby Sands Wind Farm, one of the UK's first commercial offshore wind farms, has the capability to supply 41,000 homes with energy. The visitor centre (June–Oct; free) has information on renewable energy. In summer boat trips leave regularly from Great Yarmouth beach to see the seals who bask on Scroby Sands bank – look for chalked-up signs on the beach.

Maritime Museum

Lowestoft's excellent little **Maritime Museum** ❼ (tel: 01502-561 963; http://lowestoftmaritimemuseum.org.uk; mid Apr–Oct daily 10am–5pm) is at the northern end of the resort, in a flint cottage below the lighthouse. From East Point Pavilion it's about 35 minutes on foot, or a short drive through the town. Displays cover Lowestoft's maritime history from fishing village to thriving port, with model boats, archive film footage and plenty of hands-on attractions for children.

OULTON BROAD

Lowestoft has abundant aquatic attractions but the most popular is **Oulton Broad** ❽, the southern gateway to the Broads, just 2 miles (3km) inland from Lowestoft beach. You can hire a self-drive boat for the day to explore the Broad and the River Waveney or hop on the *Waveney Princess* (tel: 01502-574 903; www.waveneyrivertours.com) for broad and river cruises. In July and August the company runs a sunset cruise (Thu and Sat) to the Aldeby Marshes where barn owls are often seen hunting.

BECCLES

From Lowestoft take the A146 to **Beccles** ❾. Formerly a flourishing Saxon sea port, it is today an appealing market town and the gateway to the Southern Broads. The dominant monument is the **Church of St Michael**, where Nelson's parents married. The handsome bell tower stands detached and offers far-reaching views from the top (guided tour only, enquire at the tourist office). Much of the activity in summer focuses on the marina, where you can feed the ducks, eat ice creams by the river or set off on a walk along the Marsh Trail. To discover the river take a trip on the *Broads Liana* or the *Big Dog* Ferry (tel: 07532-072 761; www.bigdogferry.co.uk) stopping off at the lovely **Locks Inn** at **Geldeston** ❿ *(see below)*.

Eating Out

Great Yarmouth

Olive Garden
42 Regent Road; tel: 01493-844 641; www.olivegardenrestaurant.co.uk; Mon 6–9pm, Tue–Wed noon–2pm and 5.30–9.30pm, Thu noon–2pm, Fri–Sat 5.30–10pm.
Friendly, obliging restaurant specializing in Cypriot cuisine such as beef stifado, lamb kleftiko and moussaka, along with generous helpings of other Mediterranean dishes. Sharing platters are on offer and takeaway is available. ££

The Seafood Restaurant
85 North Quay; tel: 01493-856 009; www.theseafood.co.uk; Mon–Fri noon–1.45pm and 6.30–10.30pm, Sat 6.30–10.30pm.
This outstanding fish restaurant is a family business which has been going for 34 years. All the fish is fresh and, where possible, local. Norfolk oysters, smoked fish platter or crab claws in garlic butter can be followed by monkfish, skate, turbot or brill – or, if you're pushing the boat out, one of the lobsters from the tank. £££

Somerleyton

The Duke's Head
Slugs Lane; tel: 01502-730 281; www.dukesheadsomerleyton.co.uk; food: Mon–Sat noon–2.30pm, 6.30–9pm.
This gastropub on the Somerleyton Estate *(see p.53)* places a strong emphasis on locally-sourced produce, including Welsh black beef and seasonal game from the estate. ££

Beccles

The Swan House
34 New Market; tel: 01502-713 474; www.swan-house.com; breakfast daily 8–10am by reservation, lunch daily noon–2.30pm, dinner Mon–Sat 6.45–9.30pm.
Oozing charm, The Swan House has old timbers, stripped tables and quirky art. The food is first class whether it's eggs Benedict or French toast at breakfast, tea-time cream teas or the full works at dinner. And, if you decide to spend a night in Beccles, there are charming guest rooms upstairs. ££

Geldeston

Locks Inn
Tel: 01508-518 414; www.geldestonlocks.co.uk; Mon–Fri noon–2.30pm and 6–9pm, Sat–Sun noon–9pm.
In former times the publican of this long-established watering hole used to look after Gelveston lock. The riverside setting, cosy beamed interior, award-winning ales and decent pub grub bring a steady stream of boaties, walkers and anglers. Despite its remote location it is often heaving on Sundays when entertainment is on offer. Most people come by boat, foot or ferry from Beccles and finding it by road can be tricky. Live music on Thursday and Saturday nights, and pagan festival celebrations throughout the year. £

Birdwatching

The expertly-managed nature reserves of Norfolk and Suffolk offer the best birding in the UK and year-round activity, including amazing flight displays of waders and wildfowl

Even if you're not a keen birdwatcher the site of an elegant avocet skimming the water or a flock of pink-footed geese filling the skies might just give you a momentary thrill. Wetlands and woodland, heathland and coast provide a huge range of habitats, for both resident and migratory species. There are some 100 nature reserves in the region, many equipped with observation hides and excellent visitor centres packed with information on local wildlife, trails, guided walks and the latest sitings chalked up on boards.

The Norfolk Broads are a haven for wildlife. Look out for grebes, herons, kingfishers, and, if very lucky you may catch a glimpse of the shy bittern or at least hear its strange booming call. Hickling Broad, with boat trips to hides, is the wildest of the Broads, its reedbeds and watermeadows the haunt of bitterns, bearded tits and marsh harriers. It's also one few places you might spot a crane. On the north Norfolk coast Cley Marshes Nature Reserve attracts a remarkable amount of birdlife all year round, including spotted redshank, avocet, spoonbills,

oyster catchers, terns and grey plover. The reserve has a large visitor centre with panoramic views. In the café you can watch the birdlife through huge picture windows. Titchwell Marsh is another outstanding reserve, whose marshes, reed and beach bring thousands of migrating birds and a variety of species all year round.

In winter spectacular flocks of waders and wildfowl make for the mudflats and lagoons of Snettisham Nature Reserve on the Wash. Just before high tide tens of thousands pack on to the banks and islands in front of the bird hides, some en route from the breeding grounds in the Arctic.

In Suffolk the lovely Minsmere is the RSPB's flagship nature reserve, established in 1947 and known for marsh harriers, avocets and bitterns. Book a boat trip here for Havergate Island, in the River Ore, famous for its breeding avocets and terns.

Above: twitchers at Dunwich Heath. **Top Left**: Northern Lapwing. **Bottom Left:** Bittern stalking at the edge of a reedbed. **Left:** avocet on the RSPB logo.

Birds to Tweet About

- **Avocet** The RSPB logo. A black and white wader, distinctive for its long upcurving beak. Its comeback from extinction in Britain was a great conservation victory in the 1940s.
- **Bearded tit** Very pretty brown long-tailed bird with a distinctive 'ping' call but tricky to spot in the reeds.
- **Bittern** Notoriously shy bird which hunts for fish, insects and frogs in reed beds. You're more likely to hear its distinctive booming call than see one.
- **Common crane** Very rare in the UK, but in recent years around nine pairs have nested in the Norfolk Broads and two at Lakenheath Fen.
- **Lapwing** Also known as a plover or peewit after its call. Distinctive crest. Endangered species.
- **Little tern** Pretty, chattering seabird which has a distinctive yellow bill with black tip.
- **Marsh harrier** Medium-sized bird of prey, mainly seen over reedbeds and marshes.
- **Pink-footed goose** Produces high-pitched honking calls. Numbers are on the increase.
- **Stone curlew** Crow-sized, with long yellow legs, largely nocturnal. Rarely seen – your best chance is Weeting Heath, Norfolk.

Tour 7

Southwold and Around

This 19-mile (31km) day trip takes in picturesque Southwold, the quintessential English holiday resort, followed by coastal villages and Suffolk's top nature reserve

This whole stretch of coast, characterized by sand and shingle beaches, marshland, dunes and crumbling cliffs, is designated as an Area of Outstanding Natural Beauty. The battle with coastal erosion has been going on for centuries and most of Dunwich has been washed away. Walking and birdwatching, especially at Minsmere, are popular pursuits and Southwold makes a great base for exploring the coast.

Highlights

- Southwold beach and pier
- Church of St Edmund, Southwold
- Holy Trinity Church, Blythburgh
- Dunwich Museum
- Minsmere RSPB Nature Reserve

SOUTHWOLD

A thriving fishing port in the 16th century, **Southwold** ❶ today is a remarkably unspoilt and charmingly old-fashioned, genteel sort of resort. Set on a clifftop and swept by stiff sea breezes, it is distinctive for its open greens, created after a fire destroyed most of the town in 1659. The town retains a variety of architectural styles: Georgian and Regency houses, Victorian seafront terraces, fishermen's cottages and buildings with a marked Dutch influence, reflecting trade with northern Europe. To the east the sand and shingle beach is backed by the iconic Southwold bathing-huts; to the south sailing and fishing boats are moored by the River Blyth. The com-

Left: Punch & Judy show by Southwold Pier. **Above:** Southwold's famous bathing-huts.

bination of seaside, enticing shops, restaurants, arts venues and wonderful walks and wildlife, have lured many a Londoner, and now around half of the town's houses are second homes.

Pier

At the north end of the beach the retro **pier** ❷, with its cafés, shops and quirky amusements, is a focal point for both visitors and locals. It dates back to 1900 and has had a major revamp in recent years. Gimmicks range from traditional two-penny pushers to the eccentric Under the Pier Show, a wooden hut with slot machine inventions by local artist/engineer/humorist Tim Hunkin – his 'Whack a Banker' game is the favourite. He also devised the ingenious water clock further along, which puts on a witty little show every hour or so.

Beach and Harbour

Southwold's delightful beach huts, which fetch notoriously high prices (up to £100,000) overlook the sand and shingle beach. With fancy names like 'Chocolate Box' or 'Happy Days' they are really no more than colourful seaside sheds, where you can make a cuppa or simple meal and store your buckets, spades and sunloungers. Just inland the landlocked **lighthouse** (very occasional openings) dates from 1887 and still provides a waymark for vessels at night, visible from 15 miles (24km).

Right on the seafront is the **Southwold Sailors' Reading Room** (www.southwoldsailorsreadingroom.co.uk), a social club for retired sailors and fishermen, built in 1864 to deter them from taking to the bottle, fishing on Sundays or other unholy pursuits. This rather charming old-fashioned room, packed with maritime exhibits and open to the public, still provides a quiet retreat by the sea. To the far south lies Southwold's little **harbour** ❸, with sailing and fishing boats and shacks selling the catch of the day and seafood platters. A little rowing boat takes passengers, dogs and bikes across to Walberswick.

For a blast of adrenaline in sleepy Southwold take a half-hour trip around the bay on a speedy rigid inflatable

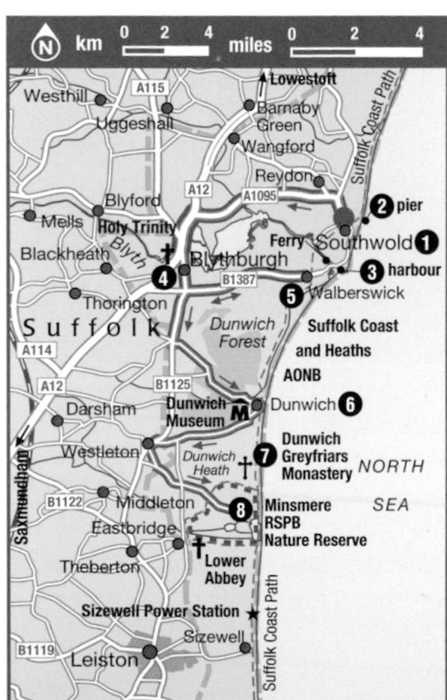

Above: the Sole Bay Inn, Southwold, known for its Adnams beers.

boat with 12 wrap-around seats (tel: 07887-525 082; www.coastalvoyager.co.uk), departing from the harbour.

Sole Bay Brewery

In the town centre follow your nose to the **Sole Bay Brewery** (tel: 01502-727 225; http://brewerytours.adnams.co.uk; daily tours) where the malty wafts of brewing Adnams ale will greet you. Beer has been sold here since 1345, though the current Brewery dates from 1872. Adnams became an integral part of Southwold, and brewery drays pulling carts packed with beer barrels were a familiar sight until 2006. Today's brewery boasts state-of-the-art machinery and is one of the greenest in the country. Friendly informative tours include a tutored tasting of beers as well as wine and gin – and a bottle of beer to take home. If you don't take the tour be sure to try the ale, available at any of the Southwold watering holes. Adnams goes from strength to strength, with a number of its own pubs and hotels, a local chain of wine merchants and a dozen Adnams Cellar & Kitchen stores. There is one round the corner on 4 Drayman Square, with the full range of Adnams beers, wines and spirits, attractive kitchenware and a good café.

Southwold Museum

Over the road from the the store, within a quaint gabled cottage, is the delightful **Southwold Museum** (tel: 01502-726 097; www.southwoldmuseum.org; daily 2–4pm; free, but donations welcome) with special exhibits on the town's former fishing industry, its emergence as a prosperous seaside resort and the rise and decline of its railway. There's also a section on the bloody but indecisive Battle of Sole Bay, fought off the coast in 1672 between the combined British and French fleets against the Dutch.

Church of St Edmund

Just to the north, across Victoria Street, is the flint-faced, copper-roofed **Church of St Edmund**, one of Suffolk's finest late medieval churches and one of the few buildings to escape the devastating town fire of 1659. The interior is light and spacious, with carved, decorated angels on the roof, a rare painted rood-screen, finely carved choirs stalls and, on a plinth just

Above: carved angles in the roof of the Holy Trinity Church, Blythburgh.

beyond the font, the little armour-clad figure known as Southwold Jack, who used to strike the bell with his battle-axe to announce the start of services.

HOLY TRINITY CHURCH, BLYTHBURGH

From Southwold take the A1095 inland, turning left on to the A12 for Blythburgh. Bear left when you see the sign 'village only', then turn right for the **Holy Trinity Church** ❹. The wool trade of this previously prosperous port left its mark in 'the Cathedral of the Marshes' as it is known. The vast church soars majestically above the Blyth estuary and can be seen for miles around. In a great storm in 1577 the church steeple crashed through the roof, killing two of the congregation. Some claim the visitor was the Devil, who left his scorch marks on the inside of the great north door. Another unwelcome visitor who left his mark was Puritan iconoclast, William Dowsing, who as Parliamentary Visitor to the Churches of Suffolk, smashed the windows and statues, fixed tethering rings to the pillars for his horses and left bullets in the timber roof. The church has beautifully carved angels decorating its tie-beam roof. Other distinctive features are the characterful poppyheads – carvings of little figures on the bench ends in the nave and the Blythburgh Jack-o'-the-Clock who once struck his bell on the hour and nowadays announces the entry of the clergy.

WALBERSWICK

From Blythburgh take the B1125 south, shortly turning left on to the B1387 for the lovely village of **Walberswick** ❺. The Anchor alone *(see*

Ⓢ Picnic on the Beach

The High Street in Southwold is a good place to pick up a picnic. The Black Olive Deli at No. 80 has fabulous home-made pies, seafood products, local cheeses, as well as olives. Just along the road The Two Magpie Bakery produces artisan bread from scratch (watch the loaves being taken from the hearth ovens), filled foccaccia and irresistible *pâtisserie*. The drink has to be the local Adnams ales, from Adnams Cellar & Kitchen, round the corner from the brewery.

Above: beer for sale at Adnams Cellar & Kitchen.

G The Walberswick Ferry

Southwold to Walberswick by car is a trip of some 7 miles (11km), via Blythburgh and the A12. But pedestrians can get there in no time via the little bridge or Walberswick Ferry across the River Blyth. This is one of the few surviving rowed ferries in the UK, operated by the fifth generation of the same family. The boat runs in season only, carries 11 passengers, plus dogs and bikes, and takes just a couple of minutes.

Above: passengers board the Walberswick Ferry.

p.65) is worth the detour. On the way into the village you'll pass **St Andrew's Church**, and the dramatic ruins beside it, which are evidence of the far grander building which once stood here. Walberswick today is a sleepy little village, and a favourite among artists for its beautiful coastal dunes, wild scenery and big skies *(see p.103)*. It is also renowned for crabbing, especially on the little bridge at 'The Flats' where children dangle pieces of bacon on string to lure up the crustaceans. In 1981 Walberswick became the home of the grandly-named British Open Crabbing Championship, drawing youngsters in their hundreds. The escalation of numbers put so much pressure on the organisers – and the stability of the local environment – that sadly the British Crabbing Federation had to terminate the event.

DUNWICH

From Walberswick return along the B1387, turning left on to the B1125 towards Leiston. After just over a mile (2km) turn left and drive through Dunwich Forest for the coastal village of **Dunwich** ❻. Seeing the tiny village today it is hard to believe that this was the medieval capital of East Anglia and one of the largest ports in England, with six churches, two monasteries, two hospitals, major shipyards and a population which was one sixth that of London. Coastal erosion was checked for 200 years by the planting of faggots, but in January 1286 a terrible storm deposited a million tonnes of sand and shingle into the harbour destroying its status as a port. Further damage was caused by the storm of 1326 and the population plummeted

Above: relaxing on Walberswick beach.

Above: Dunwich Greyfriars Monastery.

to 600. Constant erosion over the centuries has reduced the village to a handful of houses, a pub, church and a beach with a café. The population of permanent residents is down to around 60. All that remains of medieval Dunwich are the ruins of the Leper Chapel in the churchyard and those of the 13th-century **Dunwich Greyfriars Monastery** ❼ (tel: 01728-648 107; www.dunwichgreyfriars.org.uk; open year-round) on the clifftop just south of the village. This haunting monument is now managed by a charitable trust formed by local residents. A major restoration programme was completed in 2013 under the supervision of English Heritage. A solitary tombstone is the only testimony to the former presence of the medieval **All Saints Church**, which fell into the sea in 1921. Legend has it that the sound of the church bells tolling from the sea bed can be heard when a storm is threatening.

The Dunwich Museum

The **Dunwich Museum** (tel: 01728-648 796; www.dunwichmuseum.org.uk; Mar Sat–Sun 2–4.30pm, Apr–Sept daily 11.30am–4.30pm, Oct daily noon–4pm; free, but donations welcome) charts the history of the town from Roman times to the present day. The most intriguing exhibit is the scale model of Dunwich in its heyday, showing all the medieval buildings which are under the waves. The rate of loss of land is around a yard a year though this has slightly decreased in recent years.

Dunwich Heath, south of the village, is a wide expanse of heather

F Latitude Festival

Offering endless entertainment for all the family the Latitude Festival (www.latitudefestival.com) started in 2006 and is now one of the most popular festivals in East Anglia. It takes place over four days in July at Henham Park, an estate about 5 miles (8km) west of Southwold and offers a lively programme featuring music, comedy, theatre, dance, poetry and literature. Be prepared for traffic-clogged roads coming and going to the festival and book accommodation a year ahead.

Above: young revellers in the woods at Latitude Festival.

Above: walkers on Dunwich Heath.

and scrubland, commanding splendid views of the coastline (marred only by the golfball-like Sizewell B nuclear power station to the south). The heath is owned by the National Trust and is known for birdlife, but for the best sightings go straight to the neighbouring Minsmere RSPB Nature Reserve *(see below)*. For those who would like to walk but not necessarily in the fee-paying reserve, there is a well-marked, easy-going 5-mile (8km) footpath encircling the Minsmere, taking in heath, beach, marshland and woodland, and involving just 500yds/metres on a public road. You can leave the car at the park at Dunwich Heath, alternatively you could start the walk at **The Eel's Foot Inn** at Eastbridge.

> **F George Orwell**
>
> Eric Arthur Blair's family home was in Southwold and the author came back to live here in 1929–35. It was in here that he wrote his experimental novel *A Clergyman's Daughter*, the inspiration of which may have been the clergyman's daughter, Brenda Salkeld, the gym teacher at the local St Felix School, whom he fell for. In 1933 he published his more famous novel, *Down and Out in Paris and London* under the name of George Orwell – taking his surname from Suffolk's River Orwell that he so loved.

MINSMERE RSPB NATURE RESERVE

To reach Minsmere from Dunwich village by car, drive to Westleton, and follow the brown sign off the green for Minsmere. It's about 2½ miles (4km) along a narrow road, through some beautiful woodland. You don't have to be a birdwatcher to enjoy the coastal and woodland trails at the **Minsmere RSPB Nature Reserve** ❽ (tel: 01728-648 281; www.rspb.org.uk; Reserve: daily 9am–dusk; Visitor Centre: Feb–Oct 9am–5pm, Nov–Jan 9am–4pm) but it helps to enjoy nature as this is one of the best spots in the UK for wildlife. It opened in 1947 and has become increasingly popular, particularly since hosting the BBC2 wildlife series *Springwatch*.

The diverse habitats are home to an astonishing variety of birds and other wildlife. In spring and summer you might spot an avocet skimming the water, a marsh harrier 'dancing' above the reedbeds, hear the deep booming call of the bittern or glimpse the shy otter or red deer. Look out too for terns, oystercatchers and lapwings or, among the most endangered species, nightjars and bearded tits. This is a well organised reserve with a helpful visitor centre, waymarked circular trails, hides overlooking lagoons and reedbeds, guides on hand to tell you what to look out for and binoculars to hire. Youngsters can have fun in the Wild Zone, building a den, or joining in summer activities such as pond dipping and owl pellet dissection. There's a good shop too and a café with great bacon butties and home-made scones.

E Eating Out

Southwold

Lord Nelson

East Street; tel: 01502-722 079; www.thelordnelsonsouthwold.co.uk; food daily noon–2pm and 6.30–9pm.

A Southwold institution. It's cosy, close to the sea and, unsurprisingly, serves the full selection of the local Adnams beers. Expect simple home-cooked dishes (fish and chips, Thai green curry, dressed Cromer crab). The enclosed flower-decked garden is perfect for alfresco meals. £–££

Southwold Boating Lake and Tearoom

North Road; tel: 07771-781 739; www.southwoldboatinglakeandtea room.co.uk; Easter–mid-Oct daily 9.30am–4.45pm.

Friendly, 1940s-style lakeside café where you can enjoy light lunches or scrumptious cream teas sitting on Lloyd loom chairs on the lakeside verandah (warm fleecy blankets provided if it's cool) or in the quirky little tea room. £

Sutherland House

56 High Street; tel: 01502-724 544; www.sutherlandhouse.co.uk; daily noon–2.30pm and 6.30–8.30pm, closed Mon in winter.

Smart hotel restaurant where food miles are given on the menu and only seasonal ingredients are used. Try the freshly-caught fish, the award-winning black pudding sausages or the vegetable risotto with ingredients from their allotment 100yds/metres away. £££

Walberswick

The Anchor

Main Street; tel: 01502-722 122; www.anchoratwalberswick.com; daily noon–3pm and 6–10pm.

One of East Anglia's favourite gastropubs, with great beer, food, staff and a congenial setting. The chef is passionate about local food, whether it's Red Poll beef from Aldeburgh, sheep that graze near the Blyth estuary, crabs from Cromer or 'Red Herring' from Lowestoft. All the bread is home-baked. Breakfast also available. ££

The Bell

Ferry Road; tel: 01502-723 109; www.bellinnwalberswick.co.uk; daily noon–2.30pm and 6–9pm.

Ancient village pub with views over the dunes and harbour from its large garden. Decent home-made pub grub includes fish stew or pie, and Gloucester Old Spot pork belly with black-pudding faggot and bubble and squeak. ££

Dunwich

The Ship

St James Street; tel: 01728-648 219; www.shipatdunwich.co.uk; daily noon–3pm and 6–9pm.

This former smugglers' haunt, which is also a hotel, has a cosy atmosphere and good locally-sourced food. Expect home-smoked fish, ox cheeks from Bramfield, ham hock from Blythburgh and Suffolk cheese and ale fondue. £–££

Wangford

The Angel Inn

Tel: 01502-578 636; www.angelinn wangford.co.uk; daily lunch and dinner, brunch at weekends.

Come for traditional pub grub, real ales and warm Kiwi hospitality. Very good value, especially compared with pricey Southwold down the road. £

Tour 8

Aldeburgh and Around

This full-day 25-mile (40km) tour follows in the footsteps of Benjamin Britten at the well-to-do resort of Aldeburgh, then heads inland to Snape Maltings and historic sites nearby

Aldeburgh is a prosperous little town and seaside resort, with the charm of a bygone era. The town acquired international fame through the music festival, held here until 1967 when new premises were acquired at Snape. But Aldeburgh is still very much a festival centre, hosting concerts and exhibitions and accommodating Snape audiences. The composer Benjamin Britten (1913–76) spent most of his adult life in or near Aldeburgh and it was here that he wrote some of the best-known classical music of the 20th century and founded the Aldeburgh Festival *(see p.74)* with Peter Pears. With its shingle beach, boats and fish huts, Aldeburgh is a delightful spot to stay and has an exceptionally good choice of accommodation and restaurants. If you have more than a day this route could be linked to Tour 7 *(see p.58)*, covering the coast to the north.

Highlights

- Aldeburgh
- Snape Maltings
- Orford Castle
- Sutton Hoo
- Woodbridge Tide Mill

ALDEBURGH

Parking in the centre of **Aldeburgh** ❶ can be tricky but there are car parks on Thorpe Road to the north (charge) and Slaughden Quay to the south (free). Start on the waterfront in at the lovely, brick and timber-framed

Left: boats moored at Orford Quay. **Above:** the Tudor Moot Hall in Aldeburgh.

Moot Hall, a fine Tudor building which formerly stood well inland from the sea. A symbol of Aldeburgh, It has been a venue for council meetings for over 400 years and houses a small museum. Along the seafront fishermen land their glistening catch and fresh fish are sold from the huts on the steeply shelving shingle beach.

Just south of the Moot Hall, **Crag House** at 4 Crabbe Street was Benjamin Britten's seafront home from 1947–57. On the same street Jubilee Hall is a venue for concerts, the poetry festival and summer theatre.

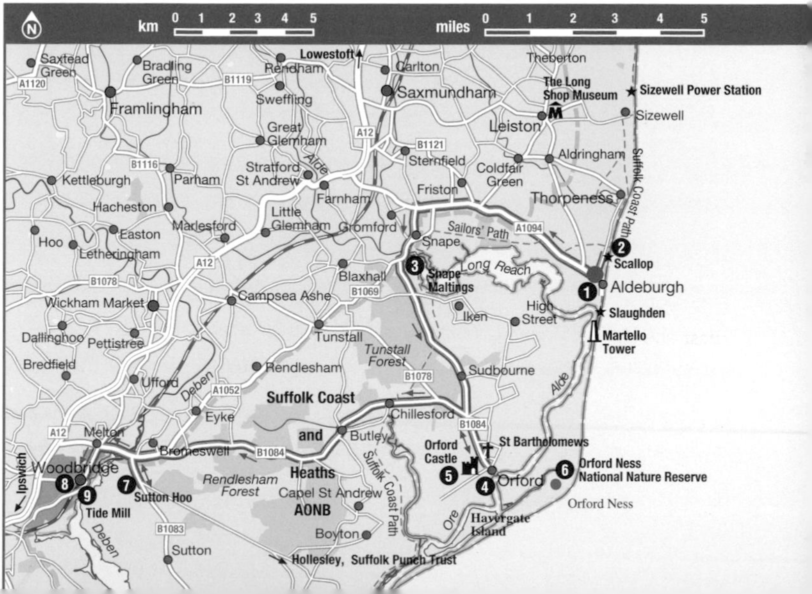

Along Crag Path, with desirable residences right on the seafront, you'll find the **Aldeburgh Beach Lookout** tower, a quirky 19th-century folly, which was sold with the proviso it must be used for artistic purposes. Sir Laurens van der Post used to write here in his later years, in the tiny room half way up. The tower was bought by Caroline Wisemen, an international art dealer who was inspired by Aldeburgh and who has turned the tower into a place where established and emerging artists can also come and be inspired by the Aldeburgh coastline. Exhibitions are held here (and in the house across the road) and Caroline offers week-long residences at the Lookout, with two rules: the artist must create new work over the course of the week, and secondly they must spend one full night in the tower. At the end of the week their creations are revealed to the public at the tower.

Running parallel with the sea, the **High Street** retains many independent shops, with appealing galleries, boutiques, delis and a wonderful book shop. Carry on walking south and you come to the clover-shaped **Martello Tower**, built, like many along the East coast in preparation for Napoleonic attacks – which never happened. It's a great place to watch the sea and can be rented as self-catering accommodation through the Landmark Trust (www.landmarktrust.org.uk).

Maggi Hambling's *Scallop*

A short walk north along the beach from the Moot Hall brings you to Maggi Hambling's huge steel ***Scallop*** ❷ dedicated to Benjamin Britten. On a heritage coast where little has changed over the years, the sculpture was a hotly controversial topic when unveiled in 2003. It has been subject to graffiti and vandalism though the attacks have abated in recent years. Locals are still divided over its aesthetic merit but it has become something of a magnet for visitors, especially for snap-happy tourists and children who like to hide behind the interlocking shells – rather than contemplating the mysterious power of the sea, which Maggi Hambling intended. If nothing else *Scallop* is a great talking point and provides excellent photo opportunities for it looks different from every angle and changes colour as you look at it. The words which are pierced through the steel and read against the sky 'I hear those voices that will not be drowned' come from Britten's opera *Peter Grimes*.

THORPENESS

A 30-minute walk or a couple of minutes' car journey along the narrow coastal road north of Aldeburgh will bring you to **Thorpeness**. This was just a fishing hamlet until it was transformed in the 1920s into a fantasy holiday haven, with a boating lake and Peter-Pan themed islands, a fairytale cottage on stilts, a country club and mock Tudor and Jacobean homes. It even had its own railway station. The entrepreneur behind the scheme was Glencairn Stuart Ogilvie, a Scottish lawyer and playwright. It was hailed as the new Suffolk seaside resort and is still very much a holiday attraction

Below: Maggi Hambling's *Scallop* on Aldeburgh beach.

Above: a room with a view – the House in the Clouds, Thorpeness.

with its 64-acre (25-hectare) boating lake, golf course and the House in the Clouds, perched on top of a water tower, and available for self-caterers who like a view.

SNAPE MALTINGS

From Aldeburgh take the A1094 heading inland, turning left for Snape after about 4 miles (6km). Formerly one of the largest barley maltings in East Anglia, Snape ceased operation in the 1960s. The 19th-century complex of red brick granaries and malt houses beside the Alde estuary were converted by Benjamin Britten into a concert hall and the Aldeburgh Festival has been held here ever since. For information and booking for the year-round concert hall programme visit www.aldeburgh.co.uk.

Snape Maltings ❸ (tel: 01728-688 303; www.snapemaltings.co.uk; daily from 10am) today is a 7-acre (3-hectare) site overlooking wildlife-rich reed beds. It's a beautiful setting, with grounds enhanced by modern sculpture, including striking works by Henry Moore and Barbara Hepworth. Snape now has a nature reserve with walks along the River Alde and boat trips in season. The shops in the converted granaries are alone worth a visit. On the food scene it has an artisan bakery, a gourmet deli, an oyster bar, an excellent café and a wonderful farmers' market every first Saturday of the month (9.30am–1pm). It is also the venue of the annual Aldeburgh Food and Drink Festival, held in the autumn. Other shops include classy boutiques, children's toys and clothes,

F Long Shop Museum

Northwest of Aldeburgh, Leiston's Long Shop Museum (www.longshopmuseum.co.uk; Mon–Sat 10am–5pm, Sun 11am–5pm) is the site of the Leiston Works, which turned the town into a prosperous manufacturing centre in the 19th century. The works were owned by Richard Garrett & Sons, who made steam tractors, cast-metal products and munitions for both World Wars. The museum charts 200 years of machinery and includes displays on the nuclear power stations at nearby Sizewell.

Above: vintage machinery on display at the Long Shop Museum.

fine furnishings, kitchenware, pottery, crafts and cards.

ORFORD

From Snape Maltings take the Snape Road south via Sudbourne to Orford (5½ miles/9km). Once a thriving port and town, **Orford** ❹ is a mere village dominated by the mighty keep of the former **Orford Castle** ❺ (tel: 01394-450 472; www.english-heritage.org.uk; Apr–Sept daily 10am–6pm, Oct daily 10am–5pm, Nov–Mar Sat–Sun 10am–4pm). The military stronghold was built by Henry II as part of a series of coastal defences in 1165. The gradual formation by the North Sea of the shingle spit (Orford Ness) led to the demise of the port and the decline of what were originally extensive castle fortifications. The castle became home to coastal defences during World War II in its life as a radar station. The 90ft (27-metre) high keep, the oldest five-sided keep in the country, soars above the village, and the top of the tower (91 steps) commands great views across to Orford Ness.

The nearby **Church of St Bartholomew**, vast in proportion to today's village, was the setting of some of the early performances by Benjamin Britten, and concerts are held here during the Aldeburgh Festival. Orford may be tiny but it is something of a foodie haven, famous for seafood and home to an oysterage, a smokehouse, a scratch bakery and Suffolk butcher, three pubs and riverside tearooms with home-made cakes. A further lure is the Crown and Castle, whose Trinity Restaurant serves up decent, unpretentious food. Just behind the Butley Orford Oysterage on Baker's Lane, follow the trail of smoke for Richardson's black, rickety **smokehouse** (Thu–Tue 10am–4pm). All manner of meats and fish are smoked here including salmon, trout, mackerel oysters, bloaters, ham hocks and duck breasts.

The road past the old Jolly Sailor Inn leads to **Orford Quay** with a hut selling fresh fish, a simple café, and, weather permitting, boat trips to Havergate Island to see avocets and other waders. Ferries take passengers from here to **Orford Ness Nature Reserve** ❻ (www.nationaltrust.org.uk), a desolate 10-mile (16km) shingle spit known for breeding and migrato-

Above: Orford Castle.

E Dining on the Alde

Spot the avocets and learn about local wildlife on the Lady Florence (tel: 07831-698 298; www.lady-florence.co.uk), a 1940s Admiralty MFV supply boat. Trips start at Orford, cruise the length of the Orford Ness conservation area and circumnavigate the RSPB's Havergate Island bird sanctuary. The maximum number of passengers is 12, there's a comfy salon, a coal fire in winter and a choice of brunch, lunch, dinner or sunset cocktail cruises, all at reasonable prices.

F Ipswich

From Woodbridge it's only 9 miles (15km) to Ipswich, the county town of Suffolk. It is a large town with unappealing outskirts, but it now has a regenerated waterfront where you can sit at cafés and watch the yachts, or take a cruise along the River Orwell. Christchurch Mansion in the eponymous park is a handsome Tudor building with a good collection of paintings by Constable and Gainsborough.

Above: Ipswich's regenerated waterfront and harbour.

ry birds. From 1913 to the mid-1980s the Ness was used as a military test site and secret experiments were carried out here. Derelict concrete buildings used for the testing are the legacy of this secret era.

SUTTON HOO

From Orford take the B1084 west towards Woodbridge. After 9 miles (15km) turn left on to the B1083 for **Sutton Hoo** ❼ (tel: 01394-389 700; www.nationaltrust.org.uk; Apr–Oct daily 10.30am–5pm, Nov–Mar Sat–Sun 11am–4pm), one of the country's most significant Anglo-Saxon sites. In 1939, just before World War II, the landowner, Mrs Edith Pretty, asked amateur archaeologist, Basil Brown, to excavate the grassy mounds on her land. The dig revealed the rotting timbers of an 89ft (27-metre) long ship, thought to have been used as the burial chamber of the Saxon King Raedwald of East Anglia in the 7th century. The ship was packed with the most priceless hoard of Anglo-Saxon treasure ever discovered. Sadly you can't see it here as it was taken to the British Museum for safekeeping.

Below: Anglo-Saxon shield replica at Sutton Hoo.

The site nevertheless has a fascinating exhibition, with replicas of the treasure, including the famous silver and gold ceremonial helmet which is the symbol of Sutton Hoo. The audio-guides feature Basil Brown himself describing the dig. Visitors can see the reconstructed burial chamber, visit some of the rooms in Mrs Pretty's house, with interesting correspondence about the discovery, and wander around burial mounds. It's a beautiful site: 245 acres (99 hectares) above the River Deben, with woodland and estuary walks. The one-hour guided tours of the burial mounds are highly recom-

K The Suffolk Punch Trust

At the village of Hollesley, south-east of Woodbridge, the Suffolk Punch Trust (tel: 01394-411 327; www.suffolkpunchtrust.org; check website for opening hours) is an educational and environmental charity dedicated to breeding and preserving the Suffolk Punch horse and its links with East Anglia's rural heritage. There's plenty for children, with stallions, mares and foals, along with rare breeds of pigs, sheep and chickens, a pets paddock, play area, garden, country walks and a good café.

Above: a Suffolk Punch in the snow.

mended but, with or without the tour, allow at least a couple of hours for the whole site.

WOODBRIDGE

The unspoilt town of **Woodbridge** 8 lies just across the River Deben. From Sutton Hoo take the B1083 north, and turn left at the roundabout on to the A1152. In Tudor times the town was a flourishing centre for shipbuilding, sail-making and weaving. Large boats can no longer navigate the River Deben, but this is still a favourite spot among the boating fraternity, with much of the activity focussing on the busy quayside and yacht harbour. It's also a delightful market town, full of small retailers (its slogan is 'Choose Woodbridge for real shopping') and a haven for gourmets with many tempting delis, cafés and restaurants.

The Tide Mill

On the River Deben quayside lies the white clapboard **Tide Mill** 9 (Tide Mill Way; tel: 01394-385 295; www.woodbridgetidemill.org.uk; Easter–Oct daily 11am–4.30pm). The nearest car park is at the railway station just to the west. The mill dates from the 1790s though the site was first mentioned in 1170. Functioning until 1957 it was the last mill in the country to work by tidal power.

The mill is currently out of order (check the website for updates), but the museum has exhibits and interactive models presenting an overview of the history and working of the mill. From here you can follow a riverside walk in either direction, offering the chance to spot oystercatchers, terns,

Above: the white clapboard Tide Mill in Woodbridge.

shellduck, avocet and, if you are really lucky, one of the 'Deben seals'.

Narrow streets lead up from the quay to the town centre, well worth exploring for its Georgian streets, galleries, shops and charming **Market Hill**. The Dutch gabled Shire Hall (1575) was formerly used on the upper level as a Magistrates' Court and the ground floor as an open corn market. The little museum across the road has displays on the evolution of Woodbridge from the Anglo-Saxon settlement to the 20th century.

E Eating Out

Aldeburgh

Aldeburgh Fish & Chip Shop
226 High Street; tel: 01728-454 685; www.aldeburghfishandchips.co.uk; Mon–Thu noon–2pm and 5.30–8pm, Sat noon–8pm.
This chippie's fame has spread far and wide and some argue it's the best in the country. The fish and potatoes are local, the batter is light. All in all, it's well worth the long wait. The Golden Galleon, at 137 High Street, is part of the same family-owned business, and also has a restaurant upstairs, but it doesn't seem to get quite as many followers. £

The Lighthouse
77 High Street; tel: 01728-453 377; www.lighthouserestaurant.co.uk; daily noon–2pm and 6.30–10pm.
A favourite haunt of locals. Fish predominates on the menu, with pan-seared scallops, Lighthouse fish soup, grilled cod fillets and seabass, but there are always a couple of dishes for keen carnivores. A busy, bustling atmosphere. ££

Ye Olde Cross Keys
Crabbe Street; tel: 01728-452 637; www.aldeburgh-crosskeys.co.uk; food daily noon–2pm and 7–9pm.
Lively little pub near the seafront serving fresh seafood caught by Aldeburgh fishermen. Fish and chips is a favourite here. A large courtyard faces the sea – and there's a log fire for winter. Has an excellent choice of the local Adnams ales. £–££

Snape

Crown Inn
Bridge Road; tel: 01728-688 324; www.snape-crown.co.uk; Mon–Fri noon–2.30pm and 6–9.30pm, Sat–Sun noon–3pm and 6.30–10pm.
You can be assured of locally-grown produce at this 15th-century inn. Garry and Teresa Cook rear geese, ducks, Suffolk lamb, rare breed pigs and goats. The game is shot at nearby Campsea Ashe, the catch of the day comes from Orford and the veg from the pub's allotment at Orford. And to complete the picture, the local brewery Adnams supplies the ales. Pre- and post-concert meals available. ££

Orford

Butley Orford Oysterage
Market Hill; tel: 01394-450 277; www.pinneysoforford.co.uk; daily noon–2.15pm, Fri–Sat also 6.30–9pm.
This long-established seafood restaurant has its own smokehouse and two boats which provide a variety of locally-caught fish. Try the plump Butley Creek oysters, home-made smoked salmon paté, creamy fish pie or catch of the day. They also have a shop near the harbour called Pinney's. ££

Woodbridge

The British Larder
Orford Road, Bromeswell; tel: 01394-460 310; www.britishlardersuffolk.co.uk; Tue–Fri noon–2.15pm and 6–8.45pm, Sat noon–3pm and 6–9.30pm, Sun noon–3pm.
Gastropub near Woodbridge, owned and run by two passionate chefs who work closely with farms and suppliers in Suffolk. Expect smoked and fresh fish from Orford, pork tenderloin from Dingley Dell (Suffolk) and Mrs Temple's Binham Norfolk blue cheese. Good value set lunches. £££

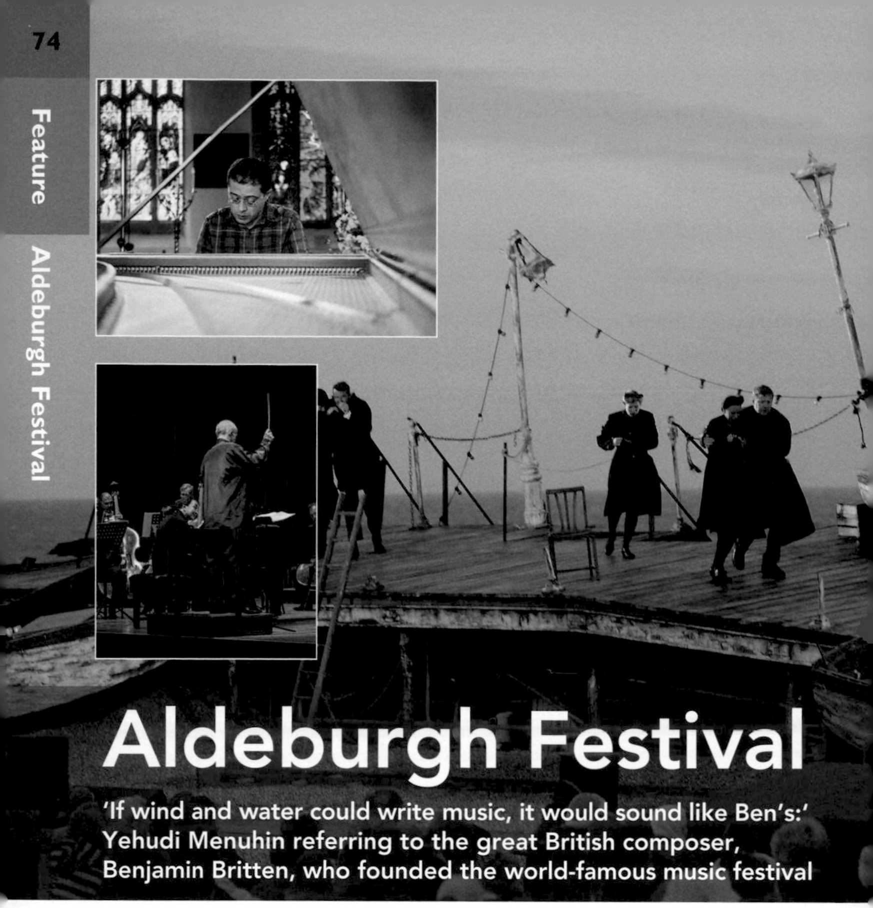

Aldeburgh Festival

'If wind and water could write music, it would sound like Ben's:' Yehudi Menuhin referring to the great British composer, Benjamin Britten, who founded the world-famous music festival

Inspired by the vast skies and ever-changing seas of the Suffolk coast, the great British composer Benjamin Britten (1912–76) lived and worked in Aldeburgh for 20 years. He was born in Lowestoft, where he started composing from a very young age, then attended Gresham's School in Holt, Norfolk, and went on to the Royal College of Music. Britten was a lifelong Pacifist and in 1939 he fled to America as a conscientious objector with the tenor, Peter Pears, his partner in both professional and private life, returning to Aldeburgh after the war. Britten and Pears lived together at Crag House in Aldeburgh but as their fame spread the house in the centre on the seafront became too much of a public attraction and they sought solitude in the more peaceful Red House, a mile from the centre.

In 1948 Britten founded the Aldeburgh Festival with Pears and the librettist Eric Crozier, bringing together international stars and emerging talent. Initially the Festival used local venues but in 1967 they converted a Victorian maltings in Snape into a 830-seat concert hall. It is now the

home of Aldeburgh Music, which has a world-wide reputation as a performance centre and offers a year-round programme of artist development and education.

The Festival, held in June, goes from strength to strength and ranks among the finest music festivals in the world. The 17-day long extravaganza is packed full of contemporary and classical music, comedy, drama, poetry and art exhibitions, but the key works are always Britten's operas. Audiences can also attend the Snape Proms in August and other events throughout the year.

Snape Maltings has other year-round attractions: stylish shops and cafés converted from riverside buildings, a nature reserve and weekly guided walks by the RSPB.

Above: *Grimes on the Beach*, performed at the Aldeburgh Festival. **Top Left**: piano recital, Aldeburgh Church. **Bottom Left:** Chamber Orchestra of Europe. **Left:** bust of Benjamin Britten, Snape Maltings.

Britten's Legacy

- **Church of St Peter and St Paul** (Church Close, above the town) Graves of Benjamin Britten and Peter Pears; Britten memorial window designed by John Piper.
- **Moot Hall** The Tudor building next to the beach was the setting for the opening scene of *Peter Grimes*.
- **Crag House**, 4 Crabbe Street. Britten's home from 1947–57.
- **Aldeburgh Jubilee Hall**, Crabbe Street. The earliest venue for the festival, and still used for events.
- **Peter Pears Gallery**, 152 High Street. Main gallery for Aldeburgh Festival exhibitions.
- ***Scallop*** On the northern beach, Maggie Hambling's controversial sculpture is dedicated to Britten. The words cut into the shell 'I hear those voices that will not be drowned' are from *Peter Grimes*.
- **The Red House**, Golf Lane (tel: 01728-451 700; www.brittenpears.org; June–Sept Tue–Sat 2–5pm; guided tours Tue–Thu and Sat 2.15pm and 3.15pm, booking required; Oct–mid-Dec Tue–Fri 2–5pm, gallery and studio only. The house where Britten and Pears lived from 1957, now home to the Britten-Pears Foundation.
- **Snape Maltings** Concert Hall operated by Aldeburgh Music, as well as stylish shops and galleries.

Tour 9

Bury St Edmunds and Around

On this full-day, 37-mile (59km) driving tour discover the historic sites of elegant Bury St Edmunds and the enticing villages of the Stour Valley to the south

The ancient market town of Bury St Edmunds was named after Edmund, the last Saxon king of East Anglia who was slain by the Danes in 869 at Hoxne on the Norfolk border. His body was brought here for reburial in 903 and pilgrims came to worship at his shrine. Today Bury is a bustling market town, with monastic ruins and a large number of historic buildings. From here it is a short drive to the beautiful villages of the Stour Valley which owe their splendour to the wool trade that flourished in former times.

Highlights

- Bury St Edmunds
- Ickworth House
- Cavendish
- Long Melford
- Lavenham

BURY ST EDMUNDS

One of East Anglia's finest towns, **Bury St Edmunds** ❶ retains Georgian and Victorian buildings, immaculate gardens and sufficient ruins to give you some idea of the scale and splendour of its former abbey. It's also a foodie's delight with more than its fair share of tempting cafés and eateries.

Start in the centre at **Angel Hill**, a square of Georgian and other buildings, overlooked by the ivy-clad **Angel Hotel**. It was here that Charles Dickens gave readings from *Nicholas Nickleby* and *David Copperfield*. He stayed at the inn in 1835, 1859 and 1861 and

Left: St Edmund's Abbey ruins.
Above: statue of St Edmund in the Abbey Gardens.

was pleased with the 'handsome little town of cleanly and thriving appearance', so much so that he organised for Mr Pickwick to visit the town a few years later. Today the Angel is a four-star boutique hotel and restaurant. On the south side the square is bordered by the **Athenaeum**, hub of social life in Georgian times.

Off Angel Hill are the immaculate and colourful **Abbey Gardens** (Mon–Sat 7.30am–dusk, Sun 9am–dusk; free) created within the walls of the former medieval monastery. Beyond the neat flower beds are the **ruins of St Edmund's Abbey**, in some cases mere mounds of rubble. The most substantial ruins are those lying behind the neighbouring Cathedral. The abbey was named after King Edmund, who was buried here, and in the Middle Ages it became one of the richest Benedictine foundations in England. It was here in 1214 that 25 barons swore to exact their rights from King John, leading to the signing of Magna Carta the following year. In 1327 the abbey was sacked by the townspeople in a protest against monastic control and the Abbey Gate was destroyed. In 1539 the abbey was dissolved and most of the buildings dismantled. The finely preserved **gatehouse** at the entrance of the gardens dates from 1347.

St Edmundsbury Cathedral

The church you see today dates back to the 15th century but was only granted Cathedral status in 1914. The Gothic-style tower lantern (seen from the far end of the nave) was built in 2005 with a grant from the Millennium Commission and local fund-raising. The tower has become a new city landmark. Exiting the cathedral you pass the **Norman Tower**, built as the main gatehouse to the abbey precincts.

St Mary's church

Next along is **St Mary's Church** (Mon–Sat 9am–4pm), built 1290–1490 as part of the abbey complex. The finest feature is the hammer-

Above: the ornate interior of the Corn Exchange, which is now a pub.

beam roof, with 11 pairs of large angels, attended by lesser angels on the wall plates, and a procession of saints martyrs, prophets and kings. It's difficult to see the detail of the dark wood but the mirrored trolley helps, or you can ask for the lights to be switched on. Behind the altar at the far end of the church lies the very simple tomb of Mary Tudor, sister of Henry VIII. Her remains were brought here from the abbey after the Reformation.

Above: an exhibit at the Moyse's Hall Museum.

Greene King Brewery

You will soon come to the **Greene King Brewery** (tel: 01284-714 297; www.greeneking.co.uk; guided tours Mon–Tue 2pm; Wed–Fri 11am and 2pm; Sat 11am, 12.30pm, 2pm and 3.30pm; Sun 11.30pm). Greene King has been brewing in Bury St Edmunds since 1799 and a guided tour gives you an interesting insight into the whole brewing process. The tour includes views of the town from the roof of the Art Deco Brew House roof and tutored tastings of the full range of beers in the Brewery tap.

Opposite the brewery the delightful **Theatre Royal** (tel: 01284-769 505; www.theatreroyal.org) is the last remaining Regency-era playhouse in the country. It is run by the National Trust and puts on a lively programme of professional and community performances.

Abbeygate and Cornhill

Return to Abbey Hill and walk up Abbeygate, a busy shopping street, to

Above: the Greene King Brewery

the **Cornhill** and **Buttermarket**. The neoclassical **Corn Exchange** is the predominant building, now occupied by a Wetherspoon pub. Nearby is **Smiths Row**, an inviting gallery of contemporary art with an affordable craft shop. Across the Cornhill **Moyse's Hall** is one of Britain's last surviving Norman houses; today it's a tourist information spot and a small town museum. Bury's market on the Cornhill and Buttermarket on Wednesday and Saturday mornings is a lively, colourful affair and one of the best in the region. Due south **The Arc** is the town's new (and controversial) shopping centre, also home to the Apex entertainment centre.

ICKWORTH HOUSE

From Bury take the A143 southwest towards Haverhill. At Horringer follow the signs for **Ickworth House** ❷ (tel: 01284-735 270; www.nationaltrust.org.uk; Rotunda: mid-Mar–Oct, Fri–Tue 11am–5pm, Thu 11am–3pm; gardens: daily 8am–8pm; Italianate Gardens 11am–5.30pm). The estate is worth visiting for the grounds alone, with eight waymarked trails for walking and cycling. The neoclassical design of the house, comprising a huge Rotunda with wings connected by curving corridors, was conceived in 1795 by the eccentric Frederick Hervey, 4th Earl of Bristol. 'When God created the human race, he made men, women and Herveys'. Attributed to Voltaire, the quote refers to the second Lord Hervey but has been used for subsequent and equally unconventional Herveys who have lived here. (The information plaques along the terrace will put you in the picture).

Today the estate is run by the National Trust. State rooms in the Rotunda are richly furnished, with

F Pint-sized Pub

The quaint Nutshell pub, by the Corn Exchange in Bury St Edmunds, has made the *Guinness World Records* as the smallest pub in the country. If you want a pint, bear in mind there's only room for around a dozen drinkers – and no space for food. One of the famous curiosities within the olde-worlde interior is the mummified black cat hanging above the bar which was found during restoration work.

Above: the landlord of The Nutshell, Britain's smallest pub.

Ⓢ Shoppers' Delight

Bury St Edmunds has an excellent market on Wednesday and Saturday mornings, and 60 percent of its shops are independently run. The prosperous wool villages have more than their fair share of antiques shops, art galleries and shops, with the occasional chic boutique. In June and July local artists open their doors for Open Studios and you can buy direct from the artist. For local produce and hand-made gifts try the town and country markets.

Above: local crafts and gifts.

vast sparkling chandeliers (each one costing £3,000 to clean!), fine portraits by Reynolds, Gainsborough and Velazquez, and a stunning collection of Georgian silver. The newly restored servants' basement gives you a good insight into downstairs life in the 1930s.

CLARE AND CAVENDISH

Turning right out of Ickworth follow the A143 for 8 miles (13km) and turn left at Stradishall (B1063), signed to **Clare** ❸. The village lies 5 miles (8km) along this road, its centre dominated by the splendid 'wool' **Church of St Peter and St Paul**. One of Suffolk's best examples of pargetting can be seen on the quaint **Ancient House** (the local museum) opposite the south porch of the church. Vestiges of the Norman keep and the old railway station buildings lie within the 25-acre (10-hectare) **Castle Country Park**, the starting point for way-marked walks.

Follow the A1092 east to the village of **Cavendish** ❹. The scene of pink thatched cottages flanking the green, and the medieval church tower rising behind, is one of the most photographed in East Anglia. In more turbulent times Wat Tyler, leader of the Peasants' Revolt in 1381, was killed at Smithfield by John Cavendish, arch enemy of the peasants, who lived in a house on the green. Cavendish was then beheaded in Bury St Edmunds by Tyler's supporters.

LONG MELFORD

Continue 4 miles (7km) along the A1092 for **Long Melford** ❺. The village derives its name from a former mill and ford, the 'Long' ap-

Above: pargetting on the Ancient House in Clare.

Above: the church and cottages on the green in Cavendish.

propriately describing the 2-mile (3km) road running through the village. This wide thoroughfare is lined by delightful 16th-century buildings, a remarkable number of them occupied by antiques shops, art galleries and specialist shops. The Perpendicular **Church of the Holy Trinity**, crowning the hill above the spacious green and seen from afar, is one of the most beautiful in Suffolk. The light-filled nave and chancel have over a hundred windows, and the north aisle has exceptionally fine stained glass, depicting friends and relatives of the Clopton family of Kentwell, the clothiers who rebuilt the church.

Melford Hall

Facing the village green is **Melford Hall** ❻ (tel: 01787-379 228; www.nationaltrust.org.uk; Apr–Oct Wed–Sun 1–5pm), a mellow red-brick Tudor mansion with six octagonal turrets. The house was devastated by fire in 1942 but restored by the Hyde Parker family whose ancestors acquired the house back in 1786. Rooms open to the public include the original banqueting hall, the Regency library and memorabilia of Beatrix Potter who was related to the family and frequently visited the hall.

Kentwell Hall

At the northern edge of the village and signposted from the green is **Kentwell Hall** ❼ (tel: 01787-310 207; www.kentwell.co.uk; house: Apr–Oct days vary, see website for details, gardens and farm: 11am–5pm, house: noon–4pm), an Elizabethan red-brick manor house. The interior was devastated by fire in the 1820s and was abandoned until the 1970s

K Step Back to Tudor England

Kentwell Hall is not just a Tudor house. History here is brought alive by Tudor re-creations, variously featuring medieval pageants, celebrations, activities and everyday life in Tudor times. Special events take place on many weekends throughout the year (see www.kentwell.co.uk for details). Youngsters can also enjoy the Hall grounds and the farm which was built from scratch in Tudor style for rare breed farm animals.

Above: tudor life re-created at Kentwell Hall.

Above: stained glass in the Church of the Holy Trinity, Long Melford.

when the present owners moved in. It has been redeveloped and today is best known for its Tudor or Victorian re-creations.

SUDBURY

Take the B1064 south for **Sudbury**, a market town on the River Stour best known as the birthplace of Thomas Gainsborough (1727–88), the great English portrait and landscape painter. His bronze statue stands at the top of the market square, and an outstanding collection of his art is on display at **Gainsborough's House** ❽ (46 Gainsborough Street; tel: 01787-372 958; www.gainsborough.org; Mon–Sat 10am–5pm, Sun 11am–5pm), a Georgian building where the artist was born and where he spent his early years. The works on display allow you to explore Gainsborough's whole career, from early portraits and local landscapes to later works from his London period. The exhibition focuses on Gainsborough's life as well as his works of art, with displays of personal memorabilia. The house runs a series of vibrant temporary exhibitions and events throughout the year, and hosts excellent print workshops and summer courses.

LAVENHAM

From Sudbury the route follows the B1115 and B1071 to **Lavenham** ❾. This is the very finest of the wool towns, preserving an extraordinary number of medieval buildings, many

Above: a carved wooden pillar on the Guildhall in Lavenham.

Above: the Little Hall in Lavenham.

of them half-timbered and tilting at alarming angles. Of the 350 buildings listed as being of architectural and historical interest, most date from between 1400 and 1500 and the old centre looks much as it did in that era. At one time this was the 14th richest town in Britain, richer than either Lincoln or York, and famous for the blue broadcloth which it exported to Europe. The town is heralded by the magnificent flint tower of the huge late Perpendicular **Church of St Peter and St Paul**. This was funded primarily by local cloth merchants and the top of the tower carries over 30 coats of arms of the Spring family, the principal wool merchants of Lavenham.

Market Place

The stunning **market place** has one of the best examples of half-timbered buildings in the country. The **Guildhall** (tel: 01787-247 646; www.nationaltrust.org.uk; Mar Wed–Sun 11am–4pm, April–Oct daily 11am–5pm, Nov Sat–Sun 11am–4pm) was the meeting place of the Guild of Corpus Christi, an organisation which regulated wool production. Since the decline of the trade, the building has variously served as a prison, workhouse, almshouse, woolstore and, during World War II, a nursery school, restaurant and home for evacuees. It has an exhibition on the wool trade and timber-framed buildings, along with an enticing Tudor tea room and garden.

Nearby **Little Hall** (tel: 01787-247 019; www.littlehall.org.uk; Apr–Oct Tue–Thu and Sat–Sun 2–4.30pm, Mon 10am–1pm) is a lovely ochre, half-timbered building owned by the Suffolk Building Preservation Trust. Built in the 14th century for a local family of clothiers it was enlarged and embellished in Tudor times. The antiques, paintings, china and other objets d'art on view today are the collection of the Gayer Anderson twin brothers, who restored the house in the 1920s.

Harry Potter Backdrop

Unsurprisingly the medieval town of Lavenham has been the backdrop of a number of films and TV series: Stanley Kubrick's *Barry Lyndon*, Michael Reeves' *Witchfinder General*, *Apothe-*

F Kersey

Beautiful old wool towns and villages are two a penny in this region. Tiny Kersey, 9 miles (14km) southeast of Lavenham, oozes charm and was described by the art historian, Nikolaus Pevsner, as 'the most picturesque village in South Suffolk'. A timeless village of timbered houses and colour-washed cottages, it is set on a steep-sided valley and crowned by the flint tower of its church. Nearby Hadleigh is a market town with some good examples of timber-framed buildings and pargetting.

osis 2 with John Lennon and Yoko Ono and the popular early 1990s TV series *Lovejoy*. More recently, in *Harry Potter and the Deathly Hallows*, Lavenham was the location for scenes in Godric's Hollow, birthplace of Harry Potter and his wizarding headmaster, Albus Dumbledore.

E Eating Out

Bury St Edmunds

Maison Bleue

30–1 Churchgate Street, tel: 01284-760 623; www.maisonbleue.co.uk; Tue–Sat noon–2pm and 7–9.30pm.

This is the best place to eat in town: outstanding locally-sourced seafood in a charming 17th-century house, with chic contemporary decor. The menu (despite the name) has Asian and unexpected twists: think Poached Colchester Gigas oysters with curry spiced chicken gateau, Italian truffle and Jerusalem artichokes. Two days' notice (and well-lined pockets) are required for the truly gastronomic *plateau de fruits de mer*. Meat dishes are also served. £££

The Old Cannon

86 Cannon Street; 01284-768 769; www.oldcannonbrewery.co.uk; food Mon–Sat noon–9pm, Sun noon–3pm.

A local brewery with an excellent brasserie menu. Some dishes are made with their own ales: beer-battered fish or the famous Gunner's Daughters sausages. Bar snacks available; it's also a B&B. £–££

The Leaping Hare Vineyard Restaurant

Wyken Hall, Stanton; tel: 01359-250 287; www.wykenvineyards.co.uk; daily noon–2.30pm, Fri–Sat also from 7pm.

This restaurant on the Wyken Hall estate, 9 miles (15km) northeast of Bury offers excellent-value meat and game from the estate, fresh fish from Lowestoft, seasonal veg grown locally and prize-winning wines from the Wyken vineyard. The setting is a 400-year-old barn, with the added bonus of the gorgeous estate gardens (Apr–Sept daily 2–6pm) with herb, knot, rose and kitchen gardens, wildflower meadows and a copper beech maze. ££

Bildeston

The Bildeston Crown

High Street; tel: 01449-740 510; www.thebildestoncrown.com; daily noon–2.45pm and 7–9.45pm.

Former coaching inn, now an award-winning hotel, restaurant and bar owned by a Suffolk farmer who produces meat from his own Red Poll herd. Choose from pub classics, house specials or, for the ultimate dining experience, the eight-course tasting menu (for the whole table). Produce, whether it's Sutton Hoo chicken or Suffolk Gold cheese, is locally sourced wherever possible. ££–£££

Long Melford

The Black Lion

The Green; tel: 01787-312 356; www.blacklionhotel.net; daily, lunch from noon, dinner from 7pm.

This historic hotel, overlooking the green lures tourists and locals alike for light lunches, clotted cream teas, full meals and Sunday roasts. Enjoy partridge pâté, estate potted hare or roast rib of beef in a very traditional English setting, with roaring log fires in winter. ££–£££

Lavenham

The Great House Restaurant

Market Place; tel: 01787-247 431; www.greathouse.co.uk; Wed–Sat noon–2.30pm, Tue–Fri 7–9pm.

One of East Anglia's top restaurants, this chic eatery offers a taste of France in a quintessentially British village. Expect mouthwatering creations such as 36-hour confit of lamb shoulder with roulade of aubergine caviar, olive cognac and basil juice. Seasonal Suffolk produce predominates. Excellent value set meals. ££–£££

Tour 10

Cambridge

On this day tour (just under 2 miles/3km), discover the city of dreaming spires and follow on with a leisurely punt along The Backs or upstream to the river village of Grantchester

In 1209, when riots in Oxford resulted in the hanging of three students, a group of its scholars settled in 'Granta Brygge' and sowed the seeds of England's second university. Prior to its rise as a celebrated seat of learning, it was a small market town on the edge of the swampy fens. The colleges which encroached on the centre were to transform it into a university-dominated town whose intellectual and architectural heritage became the envy of the world. At the same time the pre-eminence of the university gave rise to open conflicts between townspeople and students ('town and gown') which were to flare up on and off for over six centuries.

Today the university comprises 31 independent colleges, with over 16,000 students. Many visitors see no more than facades, but the true flavour of the colleges can only really be appreciated by penetrating the inner sanctums. Despite the appearance of privacy, the majority of colleges are open to the public and are more approachable than their battlemented gate-towers

Highlights

- King's College
- King's College Chapel
- The Backs
- Trinity College
- St John's College
- Fitzwilliam Museum
- Punting on the Cam

might suggest. The most famous colleges charge entrance fees and nearly all colleges have restrictions on access, particularly during the exam period (Apr–June).

Cambridge is also a market town, a shopping centre and the hub of a high-tech revolution. Over 1,500 scientific and technological companies, many based at the burgeoning 'Silicon Valley' on the northern edge of the city, benefit from the research and expertise of the university. A new science and technology campus has been built to the west of the city and the University is currently expanding further to the northwest.

KING'S COLLEGE

Start your explorations in the city centre at **King's College ❶**, which was founded in 1441 by Henry VI. It was a grandiose project involving the demolition of a quarter of the medieval centre and causing lasting anger and resentment among the townspeople. This was one of the king's two 'royal and religious' foundations, the other being Eton College, and until 1873 the College was exclusively for boys from Eton. Work on the famous King's Chapel started in 1446 and took nearly a century to complete.

Preceding Page: punting on the Cam. **Above**: the breathtaking interior of Kings College Chapel.

King's College Chapel

Normally there is no public access to the college from the main gateway, and visitors are guided to the north entrance. Facing the college facade turn right and take Senate House Passage, turning left at the end for **King's College Chapel ❷** (www.kings.cam.ac.uk/visit; term-time: Mon 9.45am–3.30pm, Tue–Fri 9.30am–3.30pm, Sat 9.30am–3.15pm, Sun 1.15–2.30pm; out of term: Mon 9.45am–4.30pm,

Ⓢ Retail Therapy

Cambridge has a busy daily market in the centre with books, jewellery and clothes as well as fruit, vegetables and cheese. The Sunday market is strong on arts, crafts and local produce. As well as the high street names in the award-winning Grand Arcade, the city has a number of interesting, small boutiques. The best hunting grounds are King's Parade, Rose Crescent, Magdalene Street and Bridge Street.

Above: a classic Cambridge satchel in an eye-catching shade of pink.

Tue–Sun 9.30am–4.30pm), world-famous for its sublime Gothic architecture and choral music.

The chapel has the largest fan-vaulted stone ceiling in the world, its only apparent support being the slender columns of the nave. The variety of decoration reflects the changes in style through five reigns and the Wars of the Roses. Dividing the ante-chapel from the choir is the intricately carved dark oak rood screen, a magnificent example of Renaissance woodwork, donated by Henry VIII. The screen bears his initials and those of his Queen, Anne Boleyn, and dates from 1533 (three years before he had her executed). Henry VIII also commissioned the exquisite stained glass windows on the north, south and east sides of the Chapel, depicting scenes from the Old and New Testament (upper and lower levels respectively). The altarpiece is Rubens' exuberant *Adoration of the Magi*, which was privately donated to the college in 1961.

Henry VI had stipulated that a choir of six men and 16 boy choristers should sing every day in the chapel. Today the renowned **King's College Choir**, whose Festival of nine Lessons and Carols is broadcast live across the world on Christmas Eve, sings here daily during term time (Mon–Sat 5.30pm, Sun 10.30am and 3.30pm) and visitors are welcome to attend the services.

THE BACKS

Visitors normally have to leave King's College Chapel by the north gate, but should the main chapel entrance

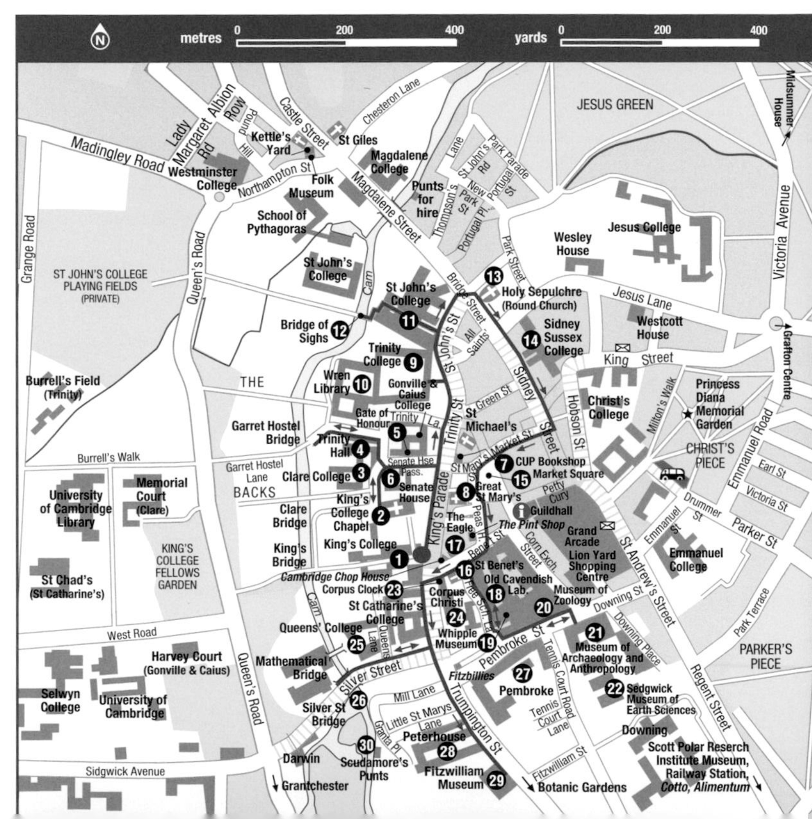

Above: view of 'The Backs'.

be open take the opportunity to see Great Court and partial views of '**The Backs**', the glorious lawns, gardens and tree-lined avenues lying between the rear of the colleges and the banks of the Cam. Exiting from the north gate you pass on your left **Clare College** ❸ founded in 1326. The college's Old Court backs onto the River Cam, and Clare Bridge – the oldest of the college bridges – offers picture-postcard views of punts drifting past weeping willows, grassy banks and college gardens. For a river view without an admission fee continue along Trinity Lane, passing **Trinity Hall** ❹, one of the smaller, more intimate colleges on the Backs, then left for **Gareth Hostel Bridge**.

Below: the Gate of Honour at Gonville and Caius College.

SENATE HOUSE PASSAGE

Retrace your steps to Senate House Passage, stopping at the **Gate of Honour** ❺ of Gonville and Caius College, one of the earliest Renaissance stone structures in the city. Undergraduates of the college pass through the gate to receive their degrees at the graduation ceremonies which take place at the **Senate House** ❻ opposite. Cross Trinity Street for the **Cambridge University Press Bookshop**, ❼ the oldest bookshop site in Britain: books have been sold here since 1581.

ST MARY THE GREAT

Across the road the **Church of St Mary the Great** ❽ has always been

an important centre of worship and debate. The great 16th-century Protestant reformers – Erasmus, Cranmer, Latimer and Ridley, who were later burnt at the stake – all preached here. It is worth climbing the 123 steps of the tower for a splendid view of the city below.

TRINITY COLLEGE

Head north along Trinity Street for the Great Gate of **Trinity College** ❾ (www.trin.cam.ac.uk; Chapel: daily 10am–5pm; Wren Library: Mon–Fri noon–2pm), the largest and richest Cambridge college, founded by Henry VIII just before his death in 1546. Trinity has produced over 30 Nobel Prize-winners, six British prime ministers, two kings and numerous poets, writers, philosophers and scientists – Francis Bacon, Lord Byron, Ernest Rutherford, Lord Tennyson and Vladimir Nabokov among them. Isaac Newton completed his best known works here and the apple tree outside the Great Gate, in front of his former study, is said to be descended from the famous tree whose apple dropped on his head and inspired the theory of gravity.

Great Court

The 16th-century **Great Court**, impressive for sheer size and grandeur, with a beautiful carved fountain, is the site of the Great Court Run, where students attempt to run round the perimeter within the time it takes the clock to strike 12 (43 seconds), a scene memorably captured in the 1981 film *Chariots of Fire* (though this was filmed at Eton, not Trinity). The Olympic runner Lord Burghley accomplished the feat in 1927. To the right of King Edward's Tower is the Gothic **Chapel**, with imposing statues of celebrated Trinity alumni in the antechapel. The large ivy-clad building on the west range is the Master's Lodge, the Master here being the only one in Cambridge who is nominated by royalty.

F Don't Walk on the Grass

This walk through Cambridge takes about two hours excluding visits to colleges and museums. If the colleges are open to the public (certain times only) it's well worth having a peek. Don't be surprised to see notices forbidding you to walk on the lawns. Only college Fellows are permitted to do so.

Above: 'keep off the grass' sign at a Cambridge college.

Above: punting under the Bridge of Sighs.

Wren Library

Great Court leads to the cloistered Nevile's Court, flanked on the far side by the **Wren Library** ⑩ (term-time: Mon–Fri noon–2pm and Sat 10.30am–12.30pm; free), one of the finest classical buildings in the country, designed by Sir Christopher Wren as a gift to the college. The four statues surmounting the library represent the disciplines of Divinity, Law, Physics and Mathematics. The perfectly proportioned interior houses rare manuscripts and first editions, with works by Shakespeare, Milton and Bertrand Russell.

ST JOHN'S COLLEGE

Leave Trinity by the Great Gate and turn left for **St John's College** ⑪ (www.joh.cam.ac.uk; daily Mar–Oct 10am–5pm, Nov–Feb 10am–3.30pm), founded by Lady Margaret Beaufort, mother of Henry VII. The 16th-century Gate Tower is a suitably ornate entrance to a college which is only challenged by Trinity for size and grandeur. Areas accessible to visitors include the very fine Tudor brick First Court, the grandiose neo-Gothic **Chapel**, inspired by Sainte-Chapelle in Paris and designed by George Gilbert Scott in the 1860s, the Tudor brick Second Court, and the delicate **Bridge of Sighs** ⑫ a Gothic revival gem modelled on its Venetian namesake. New Court was the first major College building to be erected west of the river. Known as The Wedding

Below: the Gate Tower of St John's College.

Above: enjoying an afternoon drink at the Eagle pub.

Cake, it overlooks the immaculate lawns of The Backs.

THE ROUND CHURCH AND SIDNEY SUSSEX

Exiting the college by the main entrance, turn left and cross Bridge Street for the 12th-century **Round Church** ⓭, more formally known as the Church of the Holy Sepulchre. Originally a wayfarers' chapel it is one of only four surviving Norman round churches in England. A visitor centre with information on the history of Cambridge occupies the interior.

From Bridge Street head towards the centre of town, passing on your left **Sidney Sussex College** ⓮. One of the smaller colleges, it is notable as the last resting place of the head of Oliver Cromwell. In 1960 the skull (removed from his body almost 300 years earlier) was buried here in the College chapel, but its precise location is a well-kept Cambridge secret. Cromwell had briefly been a student here, until his father's death obliged him to return home and take on family responsibilities. In 1643 he returned as military leader, looted the colleges – which supported King Charles I – and requisitioned their courts as barracks.

MARKET SQUARE AND AROUND

Turn right at the end of Sidney Street for Market Street, leading to the **Market Square** ⓯. Stalls have been trading at this square since the Middle Ages. It's a lively centre with a general market from Monday to Saturday and an arts, crafts and local produce market on Sundays. Take Peas Hill south of Market Square, to the right of the Guild Hall, and turn right into **Bene't Street**. The Saxon tower of **St Bene't's Church** ⓰ is the city's oldest architectural feature, built in about 1020 during the reign of King Canute. The round holes in the tower are thought to have been made to encourage owls to nest, and catch the mice. Opposite the church is **The Eagle** ⓱ pub, with plenty of historical interest as well as cask ales.

SCIENCE MUSEUMS

Cambridge has more museums, galleries and collections within a square

G Getting Around

Cambridge isn't car-friendly. Leave your wheels in one of the five Park and Rides (www.cambridgeshire.gov.uk/parkandride) and catch the bus into the centre. The city is relatively compact and easy to explore on foot. Alternatively, you could join the students and travel on two wheels. Bikes can be hired from Station Cycles (www.stationcycles.co.uk) on Corn Exchange Street in the centre. Or join a guided bike tour (www.cambridgebiketours.co.uk).

mile than any other UK city outside London. A cluster of them lie in the centre, though not very conspicuously. You won't have time to do them justice on a day trip but they are all free so you might just want to have a brief look and come back another day. If not, head to the Corpus Clock, below. Take **Free School Lane** beside St Bene't's Church. Half-way down is the **Old Cavendish Laboratory** ⓲ which became internationally famous for its extraordinary history of discovery and innovation in Physics. It was here that J.J. Thomson discovered the electron (1897), Ernest Rutherford split the atom (1932) and Crick and Watson discovered DNA (1950s). In 1974 the laboratory was moved to a new campus in west Cambridge.

Further down on the left is the **Whipple Museum of the History of Science** ⓳ (tel: 01223-330 906; www.hps.cam.ac.uk/whipple; Mon–Fri 12.30–4.30pm; free) with a fascinating array of scientific instruments ranging from the Middle Ages to the

Below: the Corpus Clock.

present day. Turn left at the end of the lane for Downing Street. On the left the **Museum of Zoology** ⓴ (www.museum.zoo.cam.ac.uk; closed for redevelopment until 2016; free) includes specimens discovered by Charles Darwin on his 1831 voyage on the *Beagle*.

Over the road the **Museum of Archaeology and Anthropology** ㉑ (tel: 01223-333 516; http://maa.cam.ac.uk; Tue–Sat 10.30am–4.30pm, Sun noon–4.30pm; free) displays art and culture from around the world and includes a 14-metre totem pole and Pacific material collected on Captain Cook's voyages.

Tucked away on the same site is the **Sedgwick Museum of Earth Sciences** ㉒ (tel: 01223-333 456; www.sedgwickmuseum.org; Mon–Fri 10am–1pm and 2–5pm, Sat 10am–4pm; free), housing Britain's oldest intact geological collection including a 125,000-year-old hippo found locally, marine reptiles, dinosaurs and an exhibition on 'Darwin the Geologist'.

THE CORPUS CLOCK

Return to King's Parade, on the corner with Bene't Street, where tour-

Above: the Mathematical Bridge.

ists are normally mingling around the **Corpus Clock** ㉓ on Corpus Christi's Taylor Library. This 24-carat gold-plated stainless steel disc has a large, grim-looking grasshopper perched on top which 'devours time' in front of your eyes. The clock has no hands or numerals, but there are 60 slots cut into its face which light up to show the time. The £1m time-eater was unveiled in 2008 by famous Cambridge physicist, Stephen Hawking. It was a radical idea, especially for a college whose Old Court resisted 18th-century refurbishment and is the oldest surviving enclosed court in Cambridge. For the main entrance of **Corpus Christi College** ㉔ turn left along Trumpington Street. Old Court to the left dates from 1352 and gives you an insight into the secluded and private atmosphere which characterised the early University.

QUEENS' COLLEGE

Take the next turn right, Silver Street, passing on the right **Queens' College** ㉕ (www.queens.cam.ac.uk; most days 10am–4.30pm, except during exams, check website for details). The Cam divides the college in two and is spanned by the **Mathematical Bridge**. Contrary to popular belief this was not designed by Newton, nor was it built without the use of bolts. It was in fact constructed in 1904 as an identical replacement of the original (1749) using bolts at the main joints. The College's Old Court is one of the finest examples of a medieval quadrangle, and, beyond the passage lies the enchanting Cloister Court, flanked by the half-timbered Presi-

F The Eagle's DNA

It was in the Eagle on Bene't Street in 1953 that Watson and Crick announced to the world that they had discovered 'the secret of life' (DNA). A plaque in this old coaching inn records the event, and the pub serves 'Eagle's DNA ale' to commemorate the discovery. Check out too the ceiling of the RAF Bar, covered with the names of British and American RAF pilots returning from World War II, signed with cigarette lighters and candle-smoke.

dent's Lodge. From **Silver Street Bridge** ㉖ you can see Scudamore's, pioneers of punt hire, who have been in the business for over 100 years.

PEMBROKE AND PETERHOUSE

Return to Trumpington Street and turn right. The college on the left is **Pembroke** ㉗, best known for its chapel (1663–5), the first work to be completed by Sir Christopher Wren. William Pitt the Younger (1759–1806), a precocious student, came up to Pembroke at the age of 14, and became Britain's youngest prime minister only 10 years later. Further down, on the right, is **Peterhouse** ㉘, the oldest of the colleges, founded in 1284 by the Bishop of Ely. Sir Frank Whittle, inventor of the jet engine, was a student here, as was Charles Babbage, whose work led to the modern computer.

THE FITZWILLIAM MUSEUM

Beyond Peterhouse you're unlikely to miss the formidable neoclassical facade of the **Fitzwilliam Museum** ㉙ (tel: 01223-332 900; www.fitzmuseum.cam.ac.uk; Tue–Sat 10am–5pm, Sun noon–5pm; free) one of the great treasure houses of Britain. The museum is a mini-Louvre, with almost half a million works of art from around the world. The nucleus is a priceless collection of paintings, books and manuscripts belonging to the museum's founder, Viscount Fitzwilliam. The Fitzwilliam was one of Britain's earliest public picture galleries and its internationally famous collection includes masterpieces by Italian Renaissance artists, Flemish masters and French Impressionists. There are Egyptian, Greek, Roman and West Asiatic antiquities, glass, sculpture and armour, as well as outstanding displays of ceramics, illuminated musical and literary manuscripts and a fascinating collection of fans. When it comes to a break from sightseeing there is an excellent shop with cards, books and gifts plus an adjoining café.

PUNTING ON THE CAM

One of the most enduring images of Cambridge is of languid summers

Below: paintings at the Fitzwilliam Museum.

Above: punters on the Cam.

spent punting along on the river. The calm and shallow waters of the River Cam are ideally suited to the flat-bottomed punts, which are propelled by pushing a long pole against the riverbed. Pleasure punts were introduced in Edwardian times; before that they were used by fishermen and reed cutters in the Fens. As ever, the two major university cities have their own approaches: in Cambridge, the tradition is for the punter to stand on the boat's short deck (known as the 'counter' or 'till'), whereas in Oxford, you stand at the other end, with the till at the front.

Punts can be hired at the bottom of Mill Lane at **Scudamore's** ㉚ (tel: 01223-359 750; www.scudamores.com; punt chauffeurs available). Most visitors choose to glide along The Backs behind Trinity, King's and several other colleges – though this stretch of river does become congested in summer. With time on your hands you could take the more

F Kettle's Yard

On Northampton Street, north of the city centre Kettle's Yard (www.kettlesyard.co.uk; Tue–Sun noon–5pm; free) is a fascinating little museum in four cottages, which Tate Gallery curator Jim Ede restored and made into his home in the 1950s. He filled this haven of peace with works by Ben Nicholson, Henry Moore and many other leading artists. It was an open house and one where music, light and natural objects, such as pebbles, would also greet the senses.

Above: the Kettle's Yard cottages.

G The Botanic Garden

A must for any garden lover, the Botanic Garden (www.botanic.cam.ac.uk) is a 40-acre (16-hectare) oasis providing year-round colour and structure: 8,000 plants species, a magnificent tree collection, glasshouses of tropical plants, a Water Garden, a Winter Garden and a Genetics Garden which illustrates how genetic variation plays on the appearance of plants. It's a reminder that the garden was established by Professor Henslow, the tutor who inspired Charles Darwin.

Above: one of the glasshouses in the Botanic Garden.

tranquil route through the lush meadows to Grantchester. A skilled punter should be able to reach the village in 1.5 hours or less.

Rupert Brooke's Grantchester

The riverside village of Grantchester was immortalised by Rupert Brooke, the poet who wrote movingly of the futility of war and died in World War I at the age of 28. A student of King's College, Brooke spent much of his time here, studying, swimming, walking barefoot and boating to Cambridge. The last two lines of his eulogy, 'The Old Vicarage, Grantchester', written in nostalgic mood from a Berlin café, still reverberate in the village lanes:

Stands the Church clock at ten to three
And is there honey still for tea?

It is believed the clock had broken in Brooke's day – if this was not the case it was altered to stand at ten to three for several years as a memorial to the poet. The clock today is fully functional but there is still honey for tea beneath the apple trees in The Orchard garden *(see opposite)*.

During the idyllic pre-war period The Orchard was a favourite haunt of Brooke and a group of friends, who became known as the Grantchester Group or the 'neo-pagans': the philosophers, Bertrand Russell and Ludwig Wittgenstein, the writers, E.M. Forster and Virginia Woolf, the economist, Maynard Keynes and the artist, Augustus John. Brooke lodged at Orchard House in 1909, then later moved to the old Vicarage next door, which is now home of novelist and former politician, Jeffrey Archer. Brooke, who was buried in an olive grove on the island of Skiros in Greece, is commemorated on a war memorial in the churchyard, along with other war victims.

Below: Rupert Brooke statue in Grantchester.

Eating Out

Alimentum
152–4 Hills Road; tel: 01223-41300; www.restaurantalimentum.co.uk; Mon–Sat noon–2.30pm and 6–10pm, Sun noon–2pm and 6–9pm.
Skilfully prepared yet unfussy modern European dishes are served at this seriously on-trend restaurant, which boasts a Michelin star. If you're really pushing the boat out try the 10-course chef's tasting menu. £££

Cambridge Chop House
1 King's Parade; tel: 01223-359 507; www.cambscuisine.com; Mon–Thu noon–10.30pm, Fri–Sat noon–11pm, Sun noon–9.30pm.
Right in the centre, the Chop House serves no-nonsense British classics – 'the sort of food your grandmother may have cooked' – accompanied by Cambridge real ales from the cask and wines from Languedoc-Roussillon. Despite the name there is always a fish of the day. ££

Cotto
183 East Road; tel: 01223-302 010; www.cottocambridge.co.uk; Wed–Sat 6.30–9.15pm.
The fine dining in this ex tramshed on one of the city's least attractive streets comes as something of a surprise. Chef Hans Schweitzer has worked in top-notch restaurants and his modern European dishes rarely disappoint. £££

Fitzbillies
51–2 Trumpington Street; tel: 01223-352 500; www.fitzbillies.com; Sun–Wed 10am–5.30pm, Thu–Fri 10am–9 .30pm, Sat 9am–9.30pm.
Established in 1922, this is a Cambridge institution famed for its gloriously sticky Chelsea buns. To the locals' dismay it went out of business in 2011, but has since been revitalized and is a great spot for really good coffee, delicious cakes and pastries made on the premises, and light lunches, with everything made from scratch. Simple, attractive setting and enthusiastic staff. £–££

Midsummer House
Midsummer Common; tel: 01223-369 299; www.midsummerhouse.co.uk; Wed–Sat noon–1.30pm, Tue–Thu also 7–9pm, Fri–Sat also 6.30–9pm.
Chef Daniel Clifford serves elegant, modern European cuisine in the stylish surroundings of a Victorian house on the banks of the Cam. The food is seriously sophisticated, with occasional unexpected textures and combinations. The setting is sleek and contemporary with crisp white linen and gleaming glasses. This is the only Michelin two-star restaurant in East Anglia. Go with well-lined pockets. £££

The Orchard
45–7 Mill Way, Grantchester; tel: 01223-551 125; www.orchard-grantchester.com; Mar–Oct daily 9.30am–5pm, Nov–Feb 10am–4pm.
An oasis of thought-provoking calm that became the haunt of Rupert Brooke and a remarkable group of his friends. A pamphlet lists famous people who have taken tea here, among them Bertrand Russell, E.M. Forster, Virginia Woolf, Maynard Keynes, along with royalty and 21st-century celebrities. Happily, The Orchard has changed little over the years, with its old-fashioned deckchairs under the apple trees. Coffee, teas and light lunches, inside or out. No reservations. £

The Pint Shop
10 Pea's Hill; tel: 01223-352 293; www.pintshop.co.uk; daily noon–10.30pm.
This pub and restaurant has become a hit for its beers, no-frills menu and great bar snacks. It offers 16 types of beers and 44 gins along with pies, filled cobs and Scotch eggs or delicious main meat dishes cooked over charcoal. The setting is simple (pale painted wood and parquet floors) but welcoming. £–££

Tour 11

Around Cambridge

See the high spots around Cambridge on this day tour: Ely Cathedral, the famous horse-racing centre of Newmarket and the beautiful market town of Saffron Walden

Derived from the Saxon *elge*, or eel district, Ely was formerly an inaccessible island, surrounded by marshland which seethed with eels. Following the draining of the Fenland in the 17th century, the settlement developed into a thriving market town. Today it is a prosperous little city which is completely dominated by its famous cathedral. It lies 16 miles (25km) north of Cambridge on the A10.

Highlights

- Ely Cathedral
- Newmarket National Horseracing Museum and National Stud
- Saffron Walden
- Audley End

ELY CATHEDRAL

Rising ship-like above the city and surrounding Fenland, is the magnificent Norman **Cathedral of Ely ❶** (tel: 01353-667 735; www.cathedral.ely.anglican.org; daily 7am–6.30pm, Sun until 5.30pm in winter). St Ethelreda selected this site for a Benedictine monastery for monks and nuns in AD 673. The building you see today was begun in 1083, around the time that Hereward the Wake famously used Ely as a refuge when being pursued by William the Conqueror. Eventually the monks tired of the siege and showed the conqueror's men the secret pathway through the marshes, giving Hereward away.

Inside the cathedral the sheer size takes your breath away – the nave

Left: Ely Cathedral. **Above:** the Stained Glass Museum.

is one of the longest in Britain. The crowning glory is the **timber octagon** – an octagonal tower of wood and glass built high on the back of the nave in an extraordinary feat of engineering. In the evening the lantern reflects the rays of the dying sun, by night its glass gleams with the light within. For best views join one of the guided tours (roughly every hour) which take you to the top of the Octagon (165 steps) and also up the **West Tower** (288 steps) with great views of the Fens. The **Lady Chapel**, largest of its kind in the country, formerly glowed with medieval stained-glass windows, but these, along with heads of the statuettes, were destroyed during the Reformation. The **Stained Glass Museum** (www.stainedglassmuseum.com) traces the history of stained glass from 1200 to the present day and demonstrates glass-making techniques.

NEWMARKET

Return to the A10, turn left on to the A1123, passing **Wicken Fen** *(see p.100)*, then right when you reach the A142 for **Newmarket** ❷. Racing here dates back to 1174, but its popularity as a horseracing centre grew when Charles I, who inaugurated the first cup race in 1634, firmly established it as the 'sport of kings'. Newmarket became the most fashionable racecourse in the country. Today nearly 3,000 horses, including some of the country's most thoroughbred studs, are trained on Newmarket Heath. There are two magnificent race courses, the Rowley Mile,

Ⓕ Follow the Eel

Ely's eel trail is a circular way-marked walk which follows the life cycle of an eel through five works of art. The heritage trail starts at the tourist office, former home of Oliver Cromwell, then takes in the Waterside, a great spot for a boat trip, riverside walk or cream tea. Eel-themed artworks include a 9-metre (30ft) long willow eel hive, the traditional means of eel-fishing on the River Ouse.

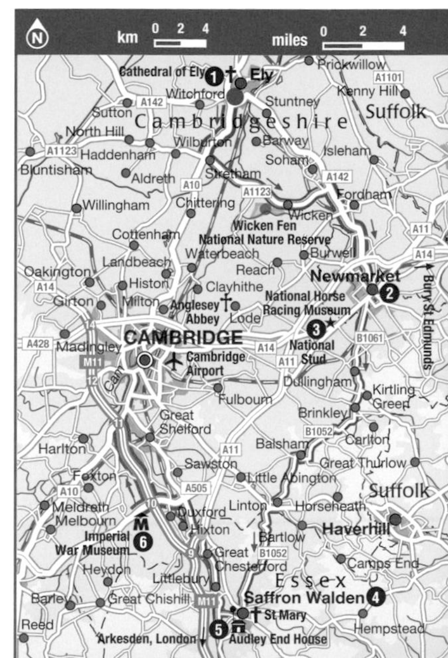

G Wicken Fen National Nature Reserve

Nine miles south of Ely, Wicken Fen (Lode Lane, Wicken, tel: 01353-720 274; www.nationaltrust.org.uk; daily 10am–5pm or dusk) is Britain's oldest nature reserve and gives you a good idea of what the Fens would have looked like before their reclamation. The site spreads over 700 acres (280 hectares), and is home to rare species of plants, insects and birds. The site has nature trails, bird hides, boat trips and cycles for hire. There is also a dragonfly centre and an old Fenland thatched cottage.

Above: Golden dragonfly at Wicken Fen Nature Reserve.

named after Charles II's favourite horse 'Old Rowley' and the July Race Course. On a weekday morning in Newmarket you can watch the racehorses training on The Gallops, the heath east of the town. There are five main flat races every year (see www.newmarketracecourses.co.uk for details).

In the centre of town the **National Horseracing Museum** (99 High Street, tel: 01638-667 333; www.nhrm.co.uk; Mar–late Dec Mon–Sat 10am–5pm, Sun 10am–4pm) gives you a good insight into the horseracing world, with all its equine memorabilia, sections on the famous and infamous who have made and lost their fortunes, the skeleton of Hyperion, the most successful British bred sire of the 20th century and a Practical Gallery where you can dress up in racing silks and take a ride on the racehorse simulator. The **National Stud** ❸ (www.nationalstud.co.uk; mid-Feb–Sept tours daily 11.15am and 2pm, Oct 11.15am only; booking essential) lies 2 miles (3km) southwest of the centre, next to the July Race Course. This the only commercial thoroughbred stud farm in the UK that allows the public to see behind the scenes. Guided tours only.

SAFFRON WALDEN

For **Saffron Walden** ❹ follow the B1061 and B1052. The town gets its name from the orange crocus dye that made it wealthy – formerly it was called Chipping Walden. Today it is a prosperous and delightfully unspoilt market town with timber-framed buildings and fine examples of pargetting, or decorative moulded plasterwork. The **Church of St Mary**, whose lofty spire can be spotted from almost

Below: Audley End House.

anywhere in town, is the largest parish church in Essex and a fine example of the Perpendicular style. A market (Tue and Sat) has been held here since 1141 and shoppers can also enjoy the many independent little shops.

AUDLEY END HOUSE

About 1 mile (1.6km) west of Saffron Walden is **Audley End House** ❺ (tel: 01799-522842; www.english-heritage.org.uk; house: Apr–Sept daily noon–5pm, Oct noon–4pm; gardens, stables and service wing: daily Apr–Sept 10am–6pm, Oct 10am–5pm; Nov–Mar Sat–Sun 10am–4pm), a grandiose Jacobean mansion set amid magnificent parkland designed by Capability Brown. The biggest house in England at the time (now half the size that it used to be) it takes its name from Sir Thomas Audley, Henry VIII's Lord Chancellor, who adapted the buildings of Walden Abbey. His grandson, Thomas Howard, Lord Treasurer to James I, turned it into a lavish mansion where he entertained the king. The 18th century saw grand changes under architects Sir John Vanbrugh and Robert Adam. But the original facade has been retained and the Great Hall preserves its huge, elaborately carved Jacobean oak screen and hammerbeam roof. Many of the state apartments have been restored to their former splendour. The Service Wing gives a fascinating insight into life 'below stairs' in Victorian times. In the grounds children can meet the horses, let off steam in the outdoor play area or take a trip on the miniature railway (end Mar–Oct Sat–Sun).

Return to Cambridge on the M11 via Duxford, home to the **Imperial War Museum** ❻ (tel: 01223-835 000; www.iwm.org.uk). Save this for another time; it could occupy an entire day!

Eating Out

Ely

The Old Fire Engine House

25 St Mary's Street; tel: 01353-662 582; www.theoldfireenginehouse.co.uk; daily 12.15–2pm, 3.30–5.15pm and 7.15–9pm, closed Sun eve.

In the shadow of Ely Cathedral, this charming Georgian house has a walled garden and a farmhouse ambience. Food is wholesome British, with seasonal local ingredients and Fenland recipes. Everything is cooked to order whether it is venison from the Denham estate, steak and kidney pie or home-cooked ham and piccalilli. Service is attentive and second helpings are usually on offer! Scrumptious cream teas too. ££

Sutton

The Anchor Inn

Sutton Gault; tel: 01353-778 537; www.anchor-inn-restaurant.co.uk; Mon–Sat noon–2pm and 7–9pm, Sun noon–2.30pm and 6.30–8.30pm.

In Fenland, 7 miles (11km) from Ely, this 17th-century inn feels quite remote but people come from far and wide for its first-class food. The emphasis is very much on seasonal and traditional ingredients, the wines are well chosen, and the setting is scrubbed pine tables and log fires, with a terrace for summer meals. It's also a good spot for walks and birdwatching. ££

Arkesden

The Axe and Compasses

The High Street; tel: 01799-550 272; www.axeandcompasses.co.uk; Mon–Sat noon–2pm and 6.30–9pm, Sun noon–2.15pm.

This traditional village pub, with thatched roof, beamed restaurant and plenty of atmosphere, is one of the most popular in the area. Food is mainly traditional British, with an emphasis on beef and fish which comes direct from Billingsgate Market. Desserts are to die for. Steak suppers on Wednesdays. ££

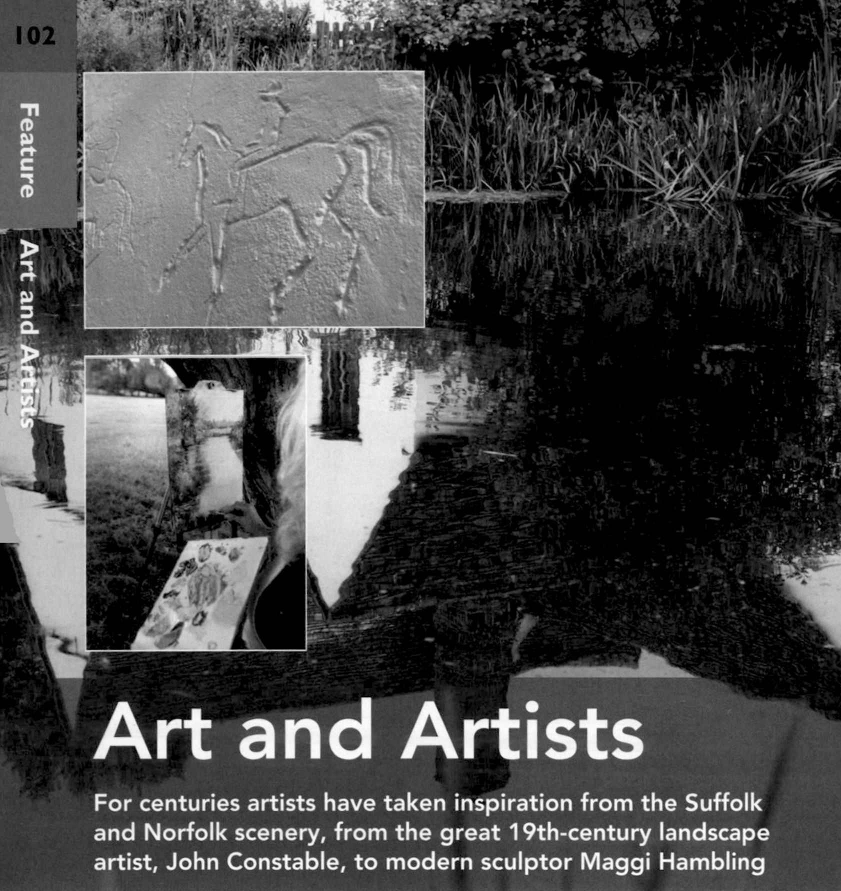

Art and Artists

For centuries artists have taken inspiration from the Suffolk and Norfolk scenery, from the great 19th-century landscape artist, John Constable, to modern sculptor Maggi Hambling

John Constable was born in East Bergholt and even when he moved to London, he would journey home frequently to sketch the valley of the Stour. 'I associate my careless boyhood with all that lies on the Banks of the Stour; those scenes made me a painter, and I am grateful'. The famous *Hay Wain* failed to receive much acclaim when exhibited in London but at the Paris Salon three years later it created a sensation. The painting had a huge influence on the development of landscape painting, especially on the French Impressionists.

Thomas Gainsborough, the great English painter of portraits and landscapes, was born in Sudbury in 1727 and most of his early work was local Suffolk scenes. Although he made his living as a painter of portraits of the aristocracy and royal family, his first love was always landscape.

Sir Alfred Munnings (1878–1959) was primarily an equestrian painter who lived in Dedham for much of his life, but he was also a portraitist and landscape artist – as you can see from the works of art in his house in Dedham, now a museum.

Where to See Art

- **Gainsborough's House**, Sudbury (www.gainsborough.org). Birthplace of Thomas Gainsborough, displaying a large collection of his works.
- **Sir Alfred Munnings Art Museum**, Dedham (www.siralfredmunnings.co.uk). Home of the equine-painter, Sir Alfred Munnings.
- **Christchurch Mansion**, Ipswich (www.cimuseums.org.uk). The largest collection of Constable's and Gainsborough's work outside London.
- **Norwich Castle Museum and Art Gallery** (www.museums.norfolk.gov.uk). The most comprehensive collection of the work of the Norwich School, covering three generations and some 50 artists.
- **Fitzwilliam Museum**, Cambridge (www.fitzmuseum.cam.ac.uk). Works by Constable, Gainsborough, the Norwich School and Maggi Hambling.
- **Aldeburgh:** Maggi Hambling's *Scallop* *(see p.68)*. Aldeburgh also has some notable galleries, including Caroline Wiseman Modern and Contemporary on Crag Path.
- **Flatford Mill:** Visit the exact spot where the artist painted *The Hay Wain* (now in the National Gallery, London).

WALBERSWICK

The Suffolk village of Walberswick has always been a favourite for artists and today has a thriving arts community. Philip Wilson Steer, the progressive British painter who looked to France for inspiration, produced seascapes of Walberswick which are regarded as some of the finest Impressionist works by an English artist. The painter rented his house next to the Bell Inn to the Scottish architect and artist, Charles Rennie Mackintosh, who painted botanical sketches around Walberswick.

Above: reflection of Willy Lott's House, Flatford. **Top Left**: horse, Sir Alfred Munnings Museum. **Bottom Left:** painter at Flatford. **Left:** Maggi Hambling's *Scallop*.

THE NORWICH SCHOOL

Founded in 1803, the Norwich School was a group of landscape artists who painted local scenes directly from nature, rather than the traditional imaginary or idealized landscapes. The leading lights were John Crome, who was self-taught and influenced by the 17th-century Dutch school and the more prolific John Sell Cotman, best known for his watercolours.

Tour 12

Colchester and Constable Country

This half-day, 15-mile (24km) tour takes in the oldest recorded town in Britain and the tranquil Stour Valley which inspired the great landscape painter, John Constable

Colchester owes its rich history to its setting on the River Colne, 8 miles (13km) from the sea. Known as Camulodunum (fortress of the Celtic war god, Camulos) it became the first capital of Roman Britain, when London was just a trading post. Queen Boudica of the Iceni tribe razed the Roman town to the ground in AD 60, before going on to do likewise in London and St Albans. The Romans rebuilt it, this time erecting a 10ft (3-metre) thick defensive wall around the city. A long section of this original town wall and the Roman gateway still stand. But the main historic attraction is the castle.

Highlights

- Colchester Castle
- Dedham Village
- Flatford Mill
- Bridge Cottage

Use either the Priory Street or Nunns Road car park for easiest access to the castle.

COLCHESTER CASTLE

William the Conqueror built the Norman castle on the ruins of the Roman Temple of Claudius. The **Norman Keep**, the largest in Britain, survives from the mighty fortress, and is home to the **Castle Museum** ❶ (High Street; tel: 01206-282 939; www.cimuseums.org.uk; Mon–Sat 10am–5pm, Sun 11am–5pm). The sheer scale of the walls is impressive, and the museum within them packs in a huge amount of information on the history of the city, from prehistory to the Civil War. After a £4 million revamp, it now has a host of interactive displays, 3D animations and numerous family activities – alongside the most important Roman British collection outside London. Displays include exquisite Roman pottery, glass, jewellery, statues and mosaics. The Colchester Vase, discovered in a grave in Colchester and decorated with four gladiators and a hunting scene, is the most famous pot from Roman Britain. The Roman vaults and the rooftop can be viewed as part of a behind-the-scenes guided tour.

CASTLE PARK

The castle forms part of **Castle Park** (daily 7.30am until dusk; free) a green oasis in the heart of the city, landscaped in the Victorian era but formerly used by farmers for grazing their sheep and cloth-makers from the Dutch Quarter for drying out their textiles. A large expanse of parkland, it has a boating pond, putting green, adventure playground and Victorian Bandstand with music most Sundays in summer. In summer it sees open air-concerts and festivals; and it's a great spot for a picnic.

At the entrance to Castle Park is the **Hollytrees Museum** (www.cimuseums.org.uk; Mon–Sat 10am–5pm, Sun 11am–5pm; free). This handsome Georgian house (which doubles up as the Visitor Information Centre) is a museum of domestic life and childhood, full of fascinating toys, costumes and decorative arts. The approach is very much a hands-on one, aimed at families. The huge dolls house is particularly popular.

Left: boats on the River Stour in Flatford. **Above:** display at the Castle Museum in Colchester.

DUTCH QUARTER

In the 16th century, Flemish weavers settled in Colchester to boost the textile trade and the town became an important weaving centre. The gabled and timber-framed houses of the peaceful **Dutch quarter** can be seen in Madenburgh Street, bordering Castle Park behind the castle (easy access

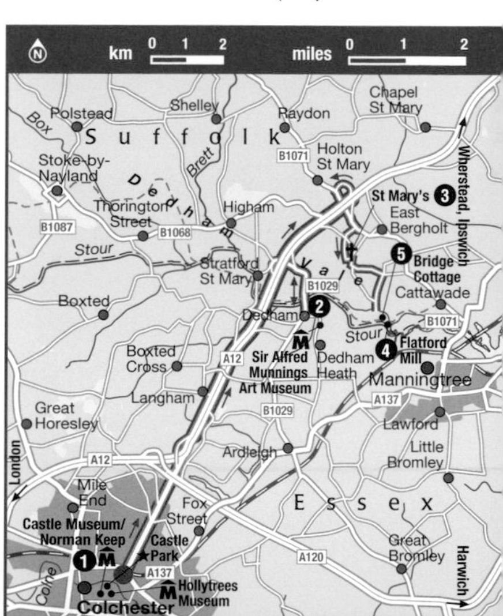

F Boudicca

Boudicca was married to Prasutagus, King of the of the Iceni tribe, who had a favoured position with the Romans and was allowed to rule independently. But when Prasutagus died the Romans turned on the Iceni, allegedly flogging Boudicca and raping her daughters. In AD 60 the flame-haired Iceni warrior led a fierce revolt, torching the three main Roman strongholds of the south, Colchester, London and St Albans. The rebellion was quashed within a year and Boudicca is believed to have taken poison to avoid capture by the Romans.

from Nunn's Rd car park). This is one of the few old quarters to survive. Colchester has seen a large amount of modern development over the years, inevitably controversial in a city so steeped in history. The best way to see its surviving historic monuments, including the oldest surviving Roman gateway in Britain, is to follow the Heritage Trail (booklet from tourist office, £2), a circular walk starting at the castle.

Above: the Church of St Mary in Dedham.

DEDHAM

From Colchester follow signs for the A12 to Ipswich, which you join 2 miles (3km) north of the city. Take the B1029 exit and follow signs for **Dedham** ❷. If there are no parking space along the main street – often the case in this popular village – follow the signs to the car park near the river. Constable used to walk daily across the River Stour from his home in East Bergholt to the grammar school in Dedham. Today it is a prosperous, quintessentially English village, the High Street lined by immaculately-preserved medieval and Georgian houses, interspersed by cafés and pubs to tempt even the most discerning of palates. The village grew rich on the wool industry, proof of which can be seen in the Marlborough Head where the original heavy beams and massive hook used to weigh the heavy fleeces and sacks of wool can still be seen.

The **Church of St Mary,** which was built in 1492–1520 with profits from the wool trade, features in several of Constable's paintings. Tom Keating, the famous art forger and art restorer, who copied some of Constable's paintings, is buried in the churchyard. Further down the High Street the United Reform church is home to the **Dedham Arts and Crafts Centre**, with a wide selection of local and other works of art and a good café.

The **Sir Alfred Munnings Art Museum** (Castle House; tel: 01206-322 127; www.siralfredmunnings.co.uk; Apr–Oct Wed–Sun 2–5pm, 11am–5pm in Aug), a mile (1.5km) further along the street, was home of horse-

Above: shoppers at the Dedham Arts and Crafts Centre.

painter Sir Alfred Munnings, and has a collection of his paintings. It can also be reached via a footpath beside St Mary's Church (allow 15 minutes).

DEDHAM VALE

A source of inspiration to Constable and other well-known British artists the tranquil **Dedham Vale** on the Suffolk-Essex border is a protected area of gently rolling fields, wooded valleys and meandering river. From the Boathouse at Dedham you can hire rowing boats, following the river as it meanders through the water meadows to Flatford, or take the *Stour Trust II*, a little electric boat, (certain days only April to October); alternatively the 1.5-mile (2.5km) footpath follows the natural line of the River Stour along pretty water meadows. By car it's a longer, circuitous route of 5.5 miles (9km).

EAST BERGHOLT

Follow the B1029 and turn left under the A12 at the Church of Stratford St Mary. Turn left again, signposted to Flatford, to join the A12. The road to **East Bergholt** (B1070) is marked off the A12. Turn right at the Carriers Arms pub. A plaque on the black railings between the church and the village shop marks the site of Constable's childhood home – this disappeared long ago. The parish **Church of St Mary** ❸ has the graves of Constable's parents and Willy Lot, whose cottage he painted. Inside, a narrow, unremarkable panel at the foot of the first stained glass window on the right commemorates the artist and his wife. The large wooden cage in the churchyard houses the heaviest

G Beth Chatto Gardens

For gardening enthusiasts there are two real gems in the region: Beth Chatto Gardens at Elmstead Market (www.bethchatto.co.uk). With her garden writing and her stunning woodland, water and gravel gardens, Beth Chatto has captivated the horticultural world for over 50 years. The Place for Plants, East Bergholt (www.placeforplants.co.uk) is a family-run garden, arboretum and plant centre, with a wonderful walled garden and a great choice of plants.

Above: a common oak tree at The Place for Plants.

Ⓕ John Constable

Constable's most famous painting, *The Hay Wain*, painted at Flatford Mill, was singled out for a gold medal by the French King Charles X, in the Paris Salon of 1824. At the time Constable's reputation was considerably higher in France than it was in England. He was not elected to the Royal Academy in London until the age of 53 (Turner was admitted at 25).

Above: Constable's *The Hay Wain*.

bells currently rung in England. The church bell tower was begun in 1525 but work ceased through lack of funds and the cage was built as a temporary protection for the bells. It has remained in the churchyard ever since and its bells are rung every Sunday.

FLATFORD

Continue past the church and follow signs for **Flatford**. From the car park (free to National Trust members) a path leads down to the River Stour. A Visitor Centre provides information on the various footpaths, including nature trails for children and riverside walks to Dedham or RSPB Cattawade Marshes.

From an early age Constable captured his rural homeland on canvas and several of his greatest works of art depict scenes which lay within a few hundred yards of his home. It is well worth taking a short guided walk (three or four a day in summer) showing you the famous scenes which he painted, comparing what you see now with reproductions of his paintings. The picturesque **Flatford Mill** ❹, best viewed from across the water, and Willy Lott's House (on the near side of the river) are both recognisable subjects of *The Hay Wain*, painted in 1821. Constable's father was a prosperous merchant who owned Flatford Mill, along with Dedham Mill, and a house, garden and windmill in East Bergholt.

Although most of the buildings are closed to the public (they are run by the National Trust and leased out to the Field Studies Council for art and environmental courses) it's a lovely spot for walking or hiring a rowing boat. But do be aware of crowds at weekends or Bank Holidays in high season.

Above: Willy Lott's House at Flatford Mill.

Bridge Cottage

The charming thatched **Bridge Cottage** ❺ (www.nationaltrust.org.uk; check website for opening times; free) lies just upstream from Flatford Mill. The cottage displays reproductions of Constable's paintings of views in the area, alongside relevant quotes from his correspondence. But most visitors soon end up in the National Trust gift shop and café for riverside cream teas, beside the dry dock where barges, known as 'lighters', were built and repaired. Seeing the river today, it is hard to believe it was formerly a busy waterway, used by the barges to transport coal, bricks, lime and corn.

Opposite the cottage is the pretty **RSPB Flatford Wildlife Garden** (Apr–Nov daily 10.30am–4.30pm; free), with flower borders, a small meadow, woodland gardens and a kitchen garden – all designed with wildlife in mind. Activities like pond-dipping and mini-beast hunting are held here in the holidays.

Ⓔ Eating Out

Colchester

The Warehouse Grill

12 Chapel Street North; tel: 01206-765 656; www.thewarehouse colchester.com; Mon 6–9.30pm, Tue–Thu noon–2.30pm, Fri–Sat noon–2.30pm and 6–10pm.

A converted chapel with a relaxed atmosphere and great burgers and steaks. Beef is matured for 28 days and served with field mushrooms, vine tomatoes, French fries or hand-cut chips. Cheap snacks also available. £–££

Dedham

The Sun Inn

High Street; tel: 01206-323 351; www.thesuninndedham.com; Mon–Thu noon–2.30pm and 6.30–9.30pm, Fri until 10pm, Sat noon–3pm and 6.30–10pm, Sun noon–3pm and 6.30–9.30pm.

A pub since the 15th century, the yellow-painted Sun has old-world charm (open fires, beams and oak panelling) and first-class food. The head chef is from Naples so expect Mediterranean flavours along with British ones. £–££

Le Talbooth

Gunhill, signposted off the A12; tel: 01206-323 150; www.milsomhotels.com/letalbooth; daily noon–2.30pm and 7–9.30pm.

Save this one for a special occasion. Part of the upmarket Milsom Hotels and Restaurants, Le Talbooth is a luxurious and beautifully-located restaurant in a half-timbered house on the banks of the Stour. Alfresco meals and riverside barbecues in summer. £££

Stratford St Mary

Hall Farm

Church Road; tel: 01206-323 600; www.hallfarmshop.com; Mon–Sat 9am–5pm, Sun 10am–4pm.

Come for breakfast, coffee and home-made cake or a leisurely lunch at this lovely family-run café-cum-deli-cum-gift shop. The deli has a great selection and is ideal for a picnic. Menus often feature prize-winning beef and lamb from the farm; bread, scones and cakes are baked daily. £–££

Wherstead

The Cookhouse

Suffolk Food Hall, Wherstead; tel: 01473-786 610; www.suffolkfoodhall.co.uk; Mon–Thu 8.30am–6pm, Fri–Sat until 10.30pm, Sun 9am–4.30pm.

It's well worth making a diversion to the award-winning Suffolk Food Hall, a food emporium that has brought together the very best of the county under one roof. With panoramic views of the Orwell Bridge and river, the restaurant serves mouth-watering 'field to fork' food, from breakfasts, light lunches to full evening meals, while the hall has an on-farm butcher, scratch baker, fishmonger, chocolatier and other irresistible Suffolk delights. £–££

Travel Tips

Active Pursuits

From cycling and swimming to fishing and golf, the region has a host of activities to keep you occupied.

WALKING

Thanks to the easy-going gently-undulating landscapes and variety of wildlife, the region is ideal for walking. Tourist information offices and visitor centres at nature reserves provide leaflets on local footpaths (often chargeable) of varying lengths. The Ordnance Survey maps, either the Explorer or Landranger series, mark footpaths and are invaluable for walkers.

Several long-distance footpaths cross the region. One of the best known is the 46-mile (74km) Peddars Way, from Knettishall Heath Country Park in Suffolk to Holme-next-the-Sea on the Norfolk coast. This joins the Norfolk Coast Path which runs from Hunstanton to Cromer, covering some 44 miles (71km) and taking in salt marshes, working fishing harbours and miles of sand dunes. The best way to explore a section of the footpath is to take a one-way walk and use the Coasthopper bus (tel: 01553-776 980; www.coasthopper.co.uk; *see p.122*) to return to your starting point. The Weaver's Way (60 miles/96km) from Cromer to Great Yarmouth takes in some of the best Norfolk Broads scenery and links with the Wherryman's Way (35 miles/56km) which connects Great Yarmouth with Norwich, mainly along the riverside.

CYCLING

With physically undemanding terrain and abundant cycle paths, both Norfolk and Suffolk are popular with cyclists. Tourist Information Centres offer a comprehensive selection of cyle leaflets and maps, many of them downloadable. The Norfolk Coast Cycleway goes all the way from King's Lynn to Great Yarmouth, and is part of the Sustrans National Cycle Network (tel: 0117-926 8893; www.sustrans.org.uk). Some of Suffolk's prettiest countryside is covered on the Cycle South Suffolk Route, designed for leisure cyclists and made up of six circular routes of varying lengths. The routes are clearly signposted all the way so you're unlikely to get lost. Parts of this route are shared with the existing National Cycle Network Hull to Harwick route. The Painter's Trail is a 69-mile (110km) route exploring the locations painted by the famous East Anglian landscape painters, which can be broken down into shorter stages. For well-organised cycling holidays in Norfolk and Suffolk contact Cycle Breaks (tel: 01449-721 555; www.cyclebreaks.co.uk). High Lodge Thetford Forest *(see Tour 2, p24)* offers highly enjoyable cycling on trails through the woodland.

BEACHES AND SWIMMING

Norfolk and Suffolk's long coastline is fringed by numerous beaches, many of them, especially on the Norfolk Coast, long and sandy. Resorts range from the archetypal bucket-and-spade destinations with sticks of rock and amusement arcades to unspoilt little hamlets by the sea where the main activity is catching crabs. On the Norfolk coast you'll find huge expanses of flat sand at Brancaster, Holkham and Wells-next-the-Sea. Many of the beaches along this coast shelve very gradually which means wading out some way before you find water deep enough for swimming. And because of the vast expanses of sand revealed at low tide it can be up to a mile (1.6km) even for a paddle. Visitors should be aware of fast incoming tides and

Preceding Pages: Go-Ape at High Lodge Thetford Forest. **Left**: Norfolk Coast Path sign. **Below:** on the beach at Wells-next-the-Sea.

One Toe in the Sea

If you're used to indoor pools or Mediterranean waters you'll find the sea temperatures on the chilly side, even in mid-summer. Most beach-goers do no more than paddle, leaving the seas delightfully crowd-free for serious swimmers. Favourite activities for youngsters are fishing around in pools when the tide goes out and catching crabs – usually with a piece of bacon tied on string. Walberswick and Blakeney are two of the most popular crabbing spots.

Above: there are some great crabbing spots along the coast.

Above: a river cruise in Suffolk on board the *Lady Florence*.

rip currents. Lifeguards operate at main resorts during the peak season. Cromer, Sheringham, Mundesley, Sea Palling are all Blue Flag beaches.

Suffolk's coast is wilder with pebbly beaches as well as some sandy ones with dunes. Two of the best beaches are Southwold Pier and Lowestoft's South Beach, both of which hold Blue Flag awards.

LEISURE CENTRES AND LIDOS

If the sea water is too cool there are always the leisure centres and the lidos. Hunstanton has the Oasis Sports and Leisure Centre (tel: 01485-534 227; www.aliveleisure.com), and Great Yarmouth's Marina Leisure Centre (tel: 01493-851 521; www.marina-centre.com) has a pool, wave machine, slide and fun sessions.

Beccles Lido (tel: 01502-714 911; www.beccleslido.com; end May–early Sept), next to the River Waveney, is a traditional, good-sized outdoor pool, heated to 80°F (27°C), with a 1-metre (3ft) springboard and a slide at the shallow end. There are separate heated toddler and paddling pools, and grassy areas for sunbathing and picnics.

BOATING

The Norfolk Broads offers all kinds of boating opportunities whether you're a seasoned sailor or have never been on a boat in your life. You can stay on a motor boat or sailing cruiser, hire a canoe or rowing boat, take a cruise with live commentary and lunch on board or a wildlife trip on a little electric boat *(see p.48)* through scenic waterways. In Suffolk one of the loveliest boat trips is the river cruise from Orford on the *Lady Florence* (tel: 07831-698 298; www.lady-florence.co.uk) offering brunch, lunch, dinner and sunset supper cruises (maximum 12 people). The boat sails year-round, with a cosy coal fire in winter, and the chance to see the elegant avocet.

Hiring a boat requires no qualifications – provided you're not sailing. Hoseasons (tel: 0844-8847 1112; www.hoseasons.co.uk/enjoy) has a large choice of cruisers, from budget boats to chic contemporary vessels, and 18 bases from which to explore the Broads. BarnesBrinkcraft (tel: 01603-782 625; www.barnesbrinkcraft.co.uk) rent out canoes and diverse leisure crafts which can be rented for an hour, half a day or a whole day.

Sailing and Surfing

The north Norfolk coast and the Norfolk Broads are both popular for sailing, and Blakeney is the favourite spot for those with their own boat. The nearby Brancaster Staithe Sailcraft Sea School (tel: 01485-210 236; www.northshore sport.co.uk) rents out sailcraft, rowing boats, kayaks and canoes; and runs sailing and powerboat courses for beginners or experienced sailors, operating in the sheltered waters of Brancaster Staithe harbour. Cromer is a popular spot for surfers, just by the pier. You can learn the skill or improve your technique at the Glide Surf School (tel: 07966-392 227; www.glidesurfschool.co.uk). In the Norfolk Broads' Hunters Yard (tel: 01692-678 263; www.huntersyard.co.uk) offer a variety of Royal Yachting Association Qualified sailing courses are offered and, for those with some experience, there are traditional wooden sailing yachts (no engine or electric power) for hire.

Above: sailing off Blakeney Point.

Canoeing

Canoeing is a wonderful way to discover the Broads and it is suitable for all the family, including young children. Canadian canoes usually carry up to three adults. Full instructions are given and buoyancy aids provided. The Canoe Man (tel: 01603-783 777; www.thecanoeman.com) in Wroxham hires out canoes and kayaks, and also offers guided canoe trails, overnight canoe

F Place your Bets

Newmarket, Great Yarmouth and Fakenham all have racecourses. Newmarket is easily the most famous with two racecourses – the Rowley Mile and the July Course. Meetings are held between April and October (visit www.newmarketrace courses.co.uk for information). Great Yarmouth stadium is East Anglia's premier greyhound racing venue with races Monday, Wednesday and Saturday evenings. It offers grandstand seating, a restaurant and four bars. Bookings required (www.yarmouthstadium.co.uk).

Above: the thrill of the race.

trails, white-water coaching and bush-craft courses.

FISHING

With its rivers and shallow lakes the Norfolk Broads is one of the best locations in the region for fishing, either from boats or angling platforms along the river banks. The Broads support a variety of freshwater fish, including roach, bream, perch, tench, eels and pike, as well as estuarine species such as flounders, sea bass and grey mullet. The coarse fishing season runs from mid-June to mid-March and a current Environment Agency licence (www.environment-agency.gov.uk) is required.

The High Lodge activity centre on the Suffolk Coast *(see p.119)* offers coarse fishing in two lakes, with carp (up to 20lbs), tench (up to 4lbs), roach and rudd. A reasonably-priced day ticket or short break pass are available. Fishing licence required.

GOLF

Norfolk and Suffolk have around 60 courses between them, catering for players of all abilities. For a list, visit www.golftoday.co.uk. In Norfolk the Royal West Norfolk (or Brancaster as it is known), Hunstanton, Royal Norwich, Royal Cromer and Sheringham rank among the best; in Suffolk top courses are Aldeburgh, Thorpeness ('Britain's Greenest golf course') Stowmarket, Woodbridge and the Royal Worlington at Bury St Edmunds and Newmarket.

There are plenty of courses which are safe and fun for junior golfers to learn and play, such as Bawburgh (www.bawburgh.com) in Norfolk which has won awards for encouraging juniors and beginners.

HORSE-RIDING

Woodlands, beaches and bridle paths make for pleasurable horse-riding in the region and tourist information centres have details of riding schools and centres. The Squirrelwood Equestrian Centre (tel: 07586-292 149; www.squirrelwoodequestriancentre.co.uk) situated between Holt and Sheringham is one of several Norfolk horse-riding centres, catering for all ages and

Below: canoeing at Blakeney.

Above: fishing at Oulton Broad.

abilities. In Suffolk the Pakefield Riding School (tel: 01502-572 257; www.pakefieldridingschool.co.uk), established in 1946, offers lessons and rides to the beach and local woods.

ACTIVITY AND THEME PARKS

Elveden Forest in Suffolk is home to one of the UK's five Center Parcs, (tel: 03448-267 723; www.centerparcs.co.uk), the award-winning holiday villages for weekends and short breaks. Lodges in the woodland sleep 2–8 and activities are abundant: zip wires through the forest, canoeing on the lake, soccer school, roller skating, fencing, fitness classes or just splashing around in the Subtropical Swimming Paradise. Activities are organised for children of all ages but there's plenty for parents to do too.

Easton Farm Park (near Woodbridge; tel: 01728-746 475; www.eastonfarmpark.co.uk) is a big hit with children who have the chance to meet Suffolk Punch carthorses, ride ponies and see baby lambs and donkey foals. In addition are barrel bug and family train rides, craft workshop, and two indoor playbarns.

Go Ape! (High Lodge, Thetford Forest; tel. 0845-519 3884; www.goape.co.uk) is an award-winning forest adventure, with zip wires, Tarzan swings and a variety of obstacles. The Tree Top Junior is designed for younger Tarzans.

Pleasurewood Hills (Leisure Way, Lowestoft; tel: 01502-586 000; www.pleasurewoodhills.com; Apr–Nov) is the biggest theme park in the East of England, offering over 20 family rides, along with half a dozen scarier thrill rides, including the region's largest rollercoaster. Booking online can save you up to 25 percent and season passes are available.

K BeWILDerwood – the Curious Treehouse Adventure

By far the best theme park in the region is BeWILDerwood (Hoveton; tel: 01692-633 033; www.bewilderwood.co.uk), a great breakthrough for sustainable UK family tourism. It is a magical playground of wobbly wires, tree houses, boat rides and jungle bridges, with weird and wonderful forest folk. Everything is built from sustainable wood and some 14,000 broad-leaf trees have been planted. A wonderful family day out which harks back to old-fashioned childhood adventures.

Above: there's fun for children and adults alike at BeWILDerwood.

Themed Holidays

From bushcraft workshops to luxury spas, a wide variety of holidays and activities are on offer in Norfolk and Suffolk.

ART AND PHOTOGRAPHY

Offering comfortable self-catering accommodation, Iken Barns (tel: 01728-688 899; www.ikenbarns.com) has a beautiful, off-the-beaten-track location, yet handy for Aldeburgh and Snape. The spacious studio overlooks the river and with a local professional artist you can paint and explore the estuary with its reedbeds, boats, birds, flora and fauna. Workshops are in small, friendly groups and all abilities, including beginners, are welcome. Book well in advance.

In a beautiful rural setting near Ludham, How Hill House is a residential Broads Study Centre and home to the How Hill Trust (tel: 01692-678 555; www.howhilltrust.org.uk), which runs residential courses on themes such as gardens, photography and wildlife.

Learn art techniques and have fun on a weekend art course with Nicola Slattery (tel: 01986-788 853; www.nicolaslattery.com) who has been running short art courses for over 20 years. Themes are likely to be printmaking, art from imagination and painting with acrylics. All levels are catered for and materials are provided along with buffet lunches. Courses take place in a pretty spot in southern Norfolk and for accommodation there are excellent farmhouses, B&Bs and old country inns nearby.

CYCLING

Cycle Breaks (tel: 01449-721 555; www.cyclebreaks.com/cycling-in-england.html) has been organising self-guided cycling tours since 1991. Cyclists just follow their maps and have their luggage taken ahead to their accommodation – usually comfortable and characterful B&Bs. There are themed itineraries and plenty of good recommendations for coffee stops, pubs and eating out.

FAMILY HOLIDAYS

South of Lowestoft, Pontins Pakefield (tel: 0871-222 0201; www.pontins.com) offers fun-packed family breaks (and ones for adults only) throughout the year. Expect simple modern accommodation and endless activities including quad bikes, pitch and putt, arts and crafts, bike hire, ball-room dancing, snooker and bingo.

Below: cycling through the Norfolk countryside.

MUSIC

Ace Cultural Tours (tel: 01223-841 055; www.aceculturaltours.co.uk) organises four-day breaks to Aldeburgh, centred around the famous Aldeburgh Festival in June. Tours include concerts, lectures and local sightseeing.

NATURE CONSERVATION

Stay in luxury tents amongst the trees at Secret Meadows Luxury Camping, (tel: 01394-382 992; www.secretmeadows.co.uk) near Woodbridge. By staying at this 115-acre (47-hectare) wildlife site, you are supporting the nature conservation charity which owns the site.

OUTDOOR ACTIVITIES

Outdoor activities on offer at Iken Barns (tel: 01728-688 899; www.ikenbarns.com) include cycling (both guided tours and tailor-made tours for independent cyclists) or paddling on a kayak to Snape or Aldeburgh. Also on offer are pony camps, bring-your-own-horse holidays, lessons in the indoor school or hacking in the local forest. You can also learn the Nordic walking technique, which purportedly burns 46 percent more calories than ordinary walking. Poles are provided. Weekend retreat breaks also available. It is advisable to book well in advance.

Not to be confused with one of the same name in Thetford Forest, the High Lodge activity centre west of Dunwich (just off the A12) offers activity breaks with clay pigeon and air rifle shooting, archery, fishing and golf, with accommodation in lake-view lodges (tel: 01986-784 347; www.highlodge.co.uk).

PAMPERING

Escape from the stresses of everyday life by booking into one of the region's Beauty Spas. A number of hotels in

Above: a guided tour of Flatford Mill.

the region, particularly in Suffolk, offer treatments: The Lifehouse Spa and Hotel in Thorpe-le-Soken (tel: 01255-860 050; www.lifehouse.co.uk), Ufford Park Hotel at Woodbridge (tel: 01394-383 555; www.uffordpark.co.uk) and Hintlesham Hall Hotel near Ipswich (tel: 01473-652 334; www.hintleshamhall.co.uk). In Norfolk the Beauty Spa at The Hoste, Burnham Market *(see p.125)* is a peaceful retreat in a chic hotel.

WALKING

British and Irish Walking Holidays (tel: 01242-254 353; www.britishandirishwalks.com) offers easy guided walks through Constable Country, a beautiful region of water-meadows, villages and churches, as immortalised by Britain's great landscape painter, John Constable. Walks include Dedham, the Stour River to Flatford Mill, East Bergholt, where Constable was born, and the villages of Stoke-by-Nayland and Nayland. B&B accommodation is at Dedham and Nayland.

Practical Information

GETTING THERE

By Road

There are good links with London and the Midlands, though neither Norfolk nor Suffolk has a motorway. From London, the South East of England, ferry ports and the Channel Tunnel the major roads to East Anglia are the M11, A11, A12, A140 and A14. The fastest route to Suffolk from London is the A12 for Ipswich, then the A12 or A14 for the rest of the county. For Norwich and Norfolk take the M11 and the A11. From the Midlands and the North the region is served by the A14, A11, A47, A17 and A1.

By Rail

For national rail enquiries visit www.nationalrail.co.uk (tel: 08457-484 950, lines open 24 hours). Abellio Greater Anglia (tel: 0345-600 7245; www.abelliogreateranglia.co.uk) runs services from London King's Cross to Cambridge, Ely and King's Lynn, and from London Liverpool Street to Colchester, Ipswich and Norwich. Connecting services are available from the Midlands, north of England and Scotland via Peterborough, including a through service from Liverpool. Book early for the best fares.

By Bus

For national coach information contact National Express (tel: 08717-818 181, lines open 24 hours; www.nationalexpress.com). Coaches travel daily to East Anglia from London (Victoria Coach Station), the Midlands and the Southeast.

By Air

The main airports for the region are Stansted (tel: 0844-335 1803; www.baa.com) and Norwich (tel: 01603-411 923; www.norwichairport.co.uk) which is just 4 miles (7km) northwest of the city centre. Both are linked by road and rail to Heathrow, Gatwick, Luton and the East Midlands airports.

By Sea

Car and passenger ferries operate between the Hook of Holland and

Above: Suffolk farmland.

Above: there is no shortage of places to visit in Norfolk and Suffolk.

Harwich with Stena Line (tel: 08447-707 070; www.stenaline.co.uk) and between Esbjerg, in Denmark, and Harwich with DFDS Seaways (tel: 08715-229 955; www.dfdsseaways.co.uk).

By Cycle

East Anglia is on the SUSTRANS National Cycle Network (tel: 0117-926 8893; www.sustrans.org.uk) Hull to Harwich (Route 1), the North Sea Cycle Route and National Route 11 which connects King's Lynn with Cambridge.

GETTING AROUND

Bus and Coach

Suffolk is served by several operators including Anglian Bus (tel: 01502-711 109; www.anglianbus.co.uk) and First Group (tel: 0871-200 2233; www.firstgroup.com). The Norfolk Coast hopper bus service *(see p.122)* operates a regular timetable between King's Lynn and Cromer.

Cycling

Cycling is an ideal way to discover the countryside. There are numerous designated cycle routes and detailed information at tourist information offices and visitor centres. Ordnance Survey maps are invaluable for cycling (and public footpaths), marking on-road and traffic-free cycle routes, both national and regional.

Rail

For timetables, ticket prices and other information visit National Rail Enquiries (tel: 08457-484 950; www.nationalrail.co.uk) or Abellio Greater Anglia (tel: 0345-600 7245; www.abelliogreateranglia.co.uk). From Norwich the Bittern and Wherry Lines (www.bitternline.com and www.wherrylines.org.uk) operate services to the coast via the Broads.

Driving

Driving can be slow, especially along the coast or getting to the coast on summer weekends and holidays. The 'A' roads link the main centres. There are some very narrow lanes connecting inland villages but driving is rarely a problem.

Car Hire

Most car hire companies will only rent to 21–75 year olds, with at least a year's experience of driving. In some cases the minimum age is 23. Shop around for special weekend and holiday rates.

Avis tel: 0808-284 5566; www.avis.co.uk.

Hertz tel: 0843-309 3099; www.hertz.co.uk.

Europcar tel: 0871-384 1087; www.europcar.co.uk.

Parking

Parking in most town centres is discouraged, but car parks are normally located within easy walking distances of the centre. As a rule the further the walk, the cheaper the parking.

Going Green

In Norfolk you can board the Bittern Line railway which runs from Norwich to Cromer or Sheringham or jump on to the Coasthopper bus (tel: 01553-776 980; www.coasthopper.co.uk) to travel between King's Lynn and Cromer. This is one of the UK's most popular rural bus services, normally operating May–Sept daily up to half-hourly, but less frequently in spring and autumn and especially winter. The combination of the Norfolk Coast Path and the Coasthopper means leaving the car behind is an easy option.

Suffolk County Council has an excellent website (www.discoversuffolk.org.uk) which promotes cycling, walking and outdoor activities, with interactive maps and downloadable walking guides and cycle maps, plus information on country parks, picnic spots, wildlife sites and bird reserves.

FACTS FOR THE VISITOR

Disabled Travellers

An increasing number of hotels and restaurants have access. At nature reserves the boardwalks are normally wheelchair friendly. There are accessible public toilets and Blue Badge parking bays across the region. Open Britain (tel: 0845-124 9971; www.openbritain.net), a website managed by the Tourism For All UK charity, provides information on accessible holiday and travel.

Emergencies

In an absolute emergency call 999 for fire, ambulance or police. Call the National Health Service number 111 when you need medical help but it is less urgent than 999. Otherwise take a taxi to the nearest casualty department of a hospital.

Entertainment

Most of the entertainment is concentrated in main towns and resorts,

Below: a trail through Ranworth Broad Nature Reserve.

Above: end-of-the-pier entertainment, Great Yarmouth.

which offer theatre and concerts. Summer festivals take place across both counties. Norwich has a good choice of drama, music or dance at the Theatre Royal or Norwich Arts Centre, and comedy at the Norwich Playhouse. Cromer on the north Norfolk coast has great variety-style shows at the end of its pier. Bury St Edmunds is home to the intimate little Theatre Royal and the new Apex Music and Entertainment Venue. Check out what's on from the tourist information websites: www.visitnorfolk.com and www.visitsuffolk.com.

Gay and Lesbian

The gay scene is mainly in the cities and towns. In Norwich The Castle (Spitalfields; tel: 01603-768 886; www.thecastle-pub.com) is billed as Norwich's Premier Gay Bar & Club. The Loft Nr1 (www.loftnr1.co.uk) is a gay nightclub with a late-night bar, terrace and dance floor, Thu–Sat only.

Opening Hours

Shops generally open Mon–Sat 9am–5.30pm, although smaller towns and villages may have a half-day closing one day a week. Large shopping centres are likely to have one evening of late-night shopping and an increasing number of shops are open on Sundays. Most banks open Mon–Fri 9.30am–4.30/5pm with Saturday morning banking common in shopping areas. Most pubs will take last drink orders at 11pm Mon–Sat and at 10.30pm on Sundays.

Tourist Information

Main tourist information offices provide (not necessarily free) pamphlets on walks and cycle trails, maps of the area and information on local attractions and events.

Aldeburgh, 48 High Street; tel: 01728-453 637; www.visit-aldeburgh.co.uk.

Cambridge, Peas Hill; tel: 0871-226 8006; www.visitcambridge.org.

Great Yarmouth, Marine Parade; tel: 01493-846 346; www.great-yarmouth.co.uk.

Hoveton/Wroxham, Station Road; tel: 01603-782 281; e-mail: hovetontic@broads-authority.gov.uk.

King's Lynn, The Custom House; tel: 01553-763 044; www.visitnorfolk.com.

Norwich, The Forum; tel: 01603-213 999; www.visitnorwich.co.uk.

Southwold, 69 High Street; tel: 01502 724 729.

Accommodation

From quirky B&Bs and boathouses to country manor houses and luxury hotels, Norfolk and Suffolk cater for all tastes. Wherever you are staying it's wise to book ahead in the summer, especially from mid-July to the end of August, and at Easter. Many hotels offer special weekend and low-season breaks between October and April.

To find the best deals book online. Most hotels include breakfast in their rates. In some of the most sought-after spots, especially on the coast, two nights will be the minimum at weekends. Bed-and-breakfasts or guesthouses, quite often in farmhouses, can offer more character and better value than hotels, with excellent home-cooked breakfasts and owners who are a mine of information on the local area.

The region offers abundant campsites, from no-frills family-run places to 'glamping' (glamorous camping) where you have the choice of yurts, tepees, gypsy caravans, bell tents and shepherds' huts, usually on eco-friendly sites in lovely locations.

Below: one of the sumptuous rooms at the Ickworth Hotel, Bury St Edmunds.

The Visit Suffolk (www.visitsuffolk.co.uk) and Visit Norfolk (www.visitnorfolk.co.uk) websites have detailed information on accommodation. Other useful sources include Norfolk Bed and Breakfasts (www.norfolk-bed-and-breakfast.co.uk) and Suffolk Bed and Breakfast (www.suffolkbedandbreakfast.co.uk).

There are numerous self-catering cottages. Norfolk Country Cottages (www.norfolkcottages.co.uk) and Suffolk Cottage Holidays (www.suffolkcottageholidays.com) have a wide selection of self-catering accommodation. For boating holidays Hoseasons (www.hoseasons.co.uk) is one of the biggest operators.

Hotels

The price bands below are a guideline for the cost of a standard en suite double room and breakfast for two people in high season.

£££ over 250
££ £150–250
£ Under £150

Aldeburgh

The Wentworth

Wentworth Road; tel: 01728-452 312; www.wentworth-aldeburgh.com.
In the hands of the same family since 1920, this is an appealing traditional hotel overlooking the beach. There are spacious seaview lounges, sea-facing gardens and roaring log fires off-season. Good food too. ££

Brudenell

The Parade; tel: 01728-452 071; www.brudenellhotel.co.uk.
The relaxing seaside atmosphere,

panoramic views and good food draw many regulars to this 4-star contemporary hotel. Guest rooms are decorated in calming colours inspired by the coast. ££

Blakeney

Blakeney Hotel

The Quay; tel: 01263-740 797; www.blakeneyhotel.co.uk.

Family-run, friendly hotel with a great quayside location overlooking the estuary and salt marshes. It's worth paying the extra for full estuary views. Restaurant, swimming pool, spa and mini-gym. ££–£££

Burnham Market

The Hoste

The Green; tel: 01328-738 777; www.thehoste.com.

Overlooking The Green in the lovely Georgian village of Burnham Market this has evolved over the years from a country inn with half a dozen simple rooms to the fashionable boutique hotel of today. Guest rooms, some of which are in village annexes, are individually decorated and range from the traditional (including room No. 5 where Nelson once stayed) to 'Divine' rooms with stylish contemporary decor and luxury bathrooms. The staff are friendly and attentive and the on-site beauty spa offers luxury pampering and relaxation. Food here is first class *(see p.35)* and the garden restaurant is delightful in summer. ££

Bury St Edmunds

Ickworth Hotel

Horringer; tel: 01284-735 350; www.ickworthhotel.co.uk.

A deluxe hotel, with self-catering as well as guest rooms, occupying the east wing of Ickworth House *(see p.79)*. It's child-friendly with family dining, a crèche, a pool, bikes to hire and 1,800 acres (728 hectares)

Above: Cley Windmill – accommodation with a difference.

of parkland for letting off steam. ££–£££

Cambridge

Hotel du Vin

15–19 Trumpington Street; tel: 0844-736 4253; www.hotelduvin.com.

Opposite the Fitzwilliam Museum, this boutique hotel occupies a fine historic townhouse. Suites are uber-luxurious, with huge beds and twin roll-top baths facing a flat-screen TV. The bistro is excellent and its wine cellars renowned. ££

Varsity Hotel & Spa

Thompson's Lane, off Bridge Street; tel: 01223-306 030; www.thevarsityhotel.co.uk.

A relative newcomer to Cambridge, the Varsity is the most stylish place to sleep in the city. It boasts a rooftop garden with views over the colleges, an impressive restaurant and a beautiful spa and gym. ££

Cley-next-the-Sea

Cley Windmill

Tel: 01263-740 209; www.cleymill.co.uk.

Oozing charm and character this is a renovated 18th-century mill with great views of the salt marshes and sea, and a friendly, private-home atmosphere. ££

Coltishall

The Norfolk Mead Hotel

Church Loke; tel: 01603-737 531; www.norfolkmead.co.uk.
Six miles (10km) from Norwich, on the edge of the Broads, this lovely country hotel reopened in 2013 under new management, and after a major revamp. Gardens extend to the banks of the River Bure, and include a walled garden, lush lawns and private lake. Guest rooms are light, airy and restful, and the award-winning restaurant makes the most of produce from local farms and markets. The breakfasts here are a great way to start the day. *£–££*

Lavenham

The Great House

Market Place; tel: 01787-247 431; www.greathouse.co.uk.
Choose from the four-poster room, grand room, Tudor Room or loft room. All are luxurious with their own unique character (and complimentary decanter of sherry). Excellent value and with one of the best restaurants in the region *(see p.84)*. *£*

Norwich

The Maids Head

20 Tombland; tel: 01603-209 955; www.maidsheadhotel.co.uk.
An historic and quirky hotel with superb location opposite the cathedral. It goes back 800 years, and claims to be the oldest hotel in Britain. The Black Prince and Catherine of Aragon are among its famous guests. Rooms vary hugely in size and style. The old ones have far more character than those in the modern extension. Street rooms can be noisy. Free parking, good restaurant. *£*

Southwold

The Angel Inn

Wangford; tel: 01502-578 636; www.angelinnwangford.co.uk.
Comfortable pub accommodation in a 16th-century former coaching inn with a relaxed, welcoming atmosphere and good affordable pub fare *(see p.65)*. Alfresco lunches and beers can be enjoyed in the large, peaceful garden. *£*

The Crown

High Street; tel: 01502-722 2275; www.adnams.co.uk/hotels.
This old inn is owned by Adnams Brewery so you know the beer will be good. There are 14 rooms in contemporary style and a popular bar-restaurant. *££*

Wells-next-the-Sea

The Crown Hotel

The Buttlands; tel: 01328-710 209; www.crownhotelnorfolk.co.uk.
A former coaching inn on a lovely leafy square, this boutique hotel has 12 stylish rooms. It is owned by celebrity chef, Chris Coubrough, so you can be assured of top-notch cuisine *(see p.42)*. *££*

Below: The Great House, Lavenham.

Index

Credits

Insight Great Breaks Norfolk & Suffolk
Written by: Susie Boulton
Edited by: Rachel Lawrence
Picture Editor: Tom Smyth
Maps: APA Cartography Department
Production: Rebeka Davies

All Images Sylvaine Poitau/Apa Publications except; BeWILDerwood 5CL, 46B, 117B; Bigstock 96T; Carys Lavin/Latitude 63B; Corrie Wingate/Apa Publications 4BR, 5TR, 36, 37, 46T, 58, 59, 62T, 76, 90T, 113CR, 115T; Getty Images 74/75; iStock 5BL, 5CR, 56TL, 56CL, 71T, 72T, 81MC, 89B, 100T, 115B; Luxury Family Hotels 124; Matt Jolly/Aldeburgh Festival 74TL, 74CL; Public domain 108T
Cover pictures by: AWL Images (T) and Dreamstime (BL & BR)

CONTACTING THE EDITORS: As every effort is made to provide accurate information in this publication, we would appreciate it if readers would call our attention to any errors and omissions by contacting:
Apa Publications, PO Box 7910, London SE1 1WE, England.
Email: insight@apaguide.co.uk
Information has been obtained from sources believed to be reliable, but its accuracy and completeness, and the opinions based thereon, are not guaranteed.

First Edition 2015
Printed in China by CTPS

Worldwide distribution enquiries:
APA Publications GmbH & Co. Verlag KG (Singapore branch)
7030 Ang Mo Kio Avenue 5
08-65 Northstar @ AMK
Singapore 569880
apasin@singnet.com.sg

Distributed in the UK and Ireland by:
Dorling Kindersley Ltd
A Penguin Group company
80 Strand, London, WC2R 0RL
sales@uk.dk.com